MW01088441

PEOPLE OF THE DUNE

PEOPLE OF THE DUNE

JIM OLSON

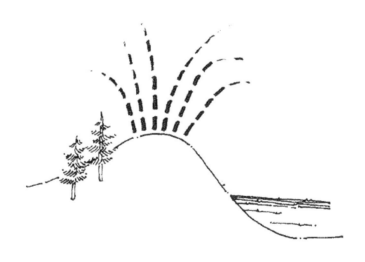

MISSION POINT PRESS

People of the Dune, Copyright © 2024
by James M. Olson

Published by Mission Point Press, Traverse City, Michigan 49696.
All U.S. and world rights reserved. Reproduction in whole or in part
without written permission is prohibited.

The author wishes mounds of thanks to the following people who
helped design, illustrate, and publish *People of the Dune*.

Illustrations: Sherry Petersen and Tajín Robles
Book and Cover Design: Heather Shaw

To order in bulk, contact www.WaterVisionsMedia.com.

ISBN: 978-1-961302-50-1
LoC: 2024907368

Printed in the United States of America.

In memory of my parents Ken Olson (1906-2001)
and Mary Helen Olson (1919-2015)
whose love for the Great Lakes inspired them to move
a young family to Northern Michigan in 1947

And in memory of Hallie (Olson) Wastell
(1972-2016) whose love for nature's beauty
nearly matched her love of family, friends,
books, music, and fashion

And:

Professor Joe Sax (1936-2014) who continues to inspire
generations of advocates to protect the gifts of earth's graces

And:

John Frey (1940-2024) whose love of nature and
philanthropy continue to bless people and the environment

CONTENTS

TO THE READER

For those who may want to explore the thoughts and ideas, expressed or unstated, in this book, an Endnote with Bibliography is provided after the Epilogue.

What will it be, the Mind or Mound?

Jim Olson
Platte River
April 2024

The designer and maker of the earth who established it,
Not as empty waste did he create it, but …
to be lived in …   Isaiah

PEOPLE OF THE DUNE

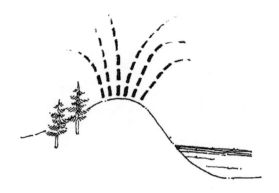

... and
on
the
third
day ...

CURRENT HEADLINES

Some, claiming direct
access to God,
said it was the fate
of the world . . .

The headlines during the past year read like an earth obituary. They had the flavor of a World War, but the obliteration, duration, enemies, victims, territories, and boundaries were not the same. Some people called it the "doom gloom." Still others blamed it all on a conspiracy of a military industrial complex that mushroomed after World War II. Then there were those claiming direct access to God, who said it was the fate of the world, the four horsemen of the apocalypse.

Most called it progress or were oblivious, too frantic with their struggle for survival. On the surface, with the turning of each day, things seemed beautiful; but the shifting of earth's deep plates pushed and grated on their nerves. People looked and acted as if they were ready to erupt. The frantic pace was a greyhound dog race: most everyone was chasing a phantom rabbit. A few wondered if it wasn't they who were the rabbits, running faster and faster to keep ahead of the dogs. Young people at the universities or those working, playing, running, scrolling, and watching the multiple screens that ran their lives, fell headlong into a future with glazed-over faces. The headlines pulsed like a strobe light into the unconscious of everyone:

NETS EMPTY

QUIET LAKE AREA GEARED UP FOR DRILLING

OIL WELL EXPLOSION DESTROYS
QUIET LAKE AREA

CORPORATE ANIMAL FARM FECES TURN LAKES
INTO DEADLY SLIME

CONGRESS EXEMPTS ANIMAL FECES
FROM WATER POLLUTION LAWS

FISH UNSAFE TO EAT

WATER UNSAFE TO DRINK

LIGHT POLLUTION DISTURBS SLEEP

TOXIC CHEMICALS LAWFUL

MULTI-NATIONAL CORPORATIONS
ROB GEORGES BANK

And:

NATURAL RESOURCE GROUP SHORT-CIRCUITS
POWER PLANT

ENDANGERED SPECIES KILL PROGRESS

PROGRESS KILLS ENDANGERED SPECIES

GREAT LAKES PIPELINE TRAMPLES ON
PUBLIC RIGHTS TO FISH AND SWIM

PRESIDENT ADOPTS WATER RULE

PRESIDENT REPEALS WATER RULE

LEGISLATORS KILL COURT
PROTECTION OF WILD AREA

DEREGULATION: NEW "MANIFEST DESTINY"

CONGRESS TAKES COFFEE BREAK

And:

ACID RAIN CAUSES BALDNESS

MOTHER EARTH TO GET ANTACID TABLET

DESIGNER JEANS TO DESIGNER GENES

EARTH TURNS TO SUN AND WIND FOR ENERGY

HEDGE FUNDS BUY UP RENEWABLE
ENERGY SOURCES

GLOBAL WARMING DISRUPTS WATER CYCLE

CITIES AND TOWNS SHUT OFF
DRINKING WATER

WATER COMPANIES BUY UP CITY
AND TOWN WATER SUPPLIES

HEDGE FUNDS BUY LAND TO CONTROL WATER

And:

LAS VEGAS ODDSMAKERS SET BET ON
NEXT WILDFIRES AND FLOODS

U.N. REPORT: EARTH NO LONGER HABITABLE

But one headline buried in the local section of a city's newspaper stood out:

ENVIROS AND TRIBES SUE TO STOP MINING OF COASTAL DUNE

RECLUSE CLAIMS SACRED MOUND BURIED UNDER DUNE

City-on-the-Bay, Michigan. A newly formed citizen's organization calling itself People of the Dune, and the Mound People Coalition, led by a band of Odawa and Ojibwa Indians, filed a lawsuit in circuit court yesterday to halt the Mython World Mining Corporation's extraction. It would remove the massive Voyager Point Dune on the waters of Lake Michigan, one of the world's great inland seas. The dune is just south of a nearby national lakeshore, named after an Odawa legend about a mother bear who eternally mourns the drowning of her cubs—cubs that now take the form of two islands off the coast.

At the end of the entrance road and across a field, the dune rises three hundred feet to reach its pinnacle. Ripples and ridges of sand, dune grass, wildflowers, and the tips of dead trees appear and disappear in the incessantly shifting sands. Birds, small animals, and deer nest and forage in valleys of hardwoods and white pines and meadows on the lee side of the dune. There are few signs of civilization, mostly old logging two-tracks.

An old recluse who says his name is Solon Creek lives alone in a two-room shack in a valley at the foot of the dune. He says he's a descendant of an ancient civilization that built a sacred mound here over 2000 years ago. He says these ancient civilizations stored food, earthen pottery, and tools, buried the bones of their dead, and held ceremonies to restore their relationship with earth and sky. He claims the mound is covered by centuries of blowing wind and sand. "There's a hump on the top of the dune there where the clump of trees grows. The top of the mound is under there," he said.

He also said he picked up something on his electromagnetic field meter he uses to search for ghosts. "But it's not the same sound," he said. Ward Stanley, a local geologist, confirmed that the dunes move inland as much as three or four feet every year, like giant waves of sand. "Sure, I've had to pull my shack back twice from getting buried by the sand," Creek said.

Project manager for Mython World Mining Corporation, Tony O'Rourke, scoffed, "Preposterous, just because someone feels something, doesn't mean it's there. The dune formed and evolved along the lakeshore after the last Ice Age. That's it. Period. We own it now."

When asked about the concerns over the impacts from mining, O'Rourke said, "The project meets all legal requirements, including thorough consideration of the harms. When it comes to mining, you must mine the sand where you find it. It's just a nibble. Won't harm the other three hundred miles of dunes." He said that, after removing the dune, the company intends to "restore" the land with a development of an artificial lake and a village of fine homes and mix of tourist-friendly businesses. "Just wait, when we're done mining, this property will be a waterfront gem, more beautiful and accessible to people than it is now."

Chelsea Charity, a leader of the People of the Dune group, disputed what O'Rourke said. "Nothing but slick sophistry. His job is to justify the destruction of the dune and its habitat. And there's no such thing as a 'nibble' when it comes to the special character of these dunes. These dunes are part of the water, the shore, our culture, our community; the dunes are part of us. When we breathe, we are part of them whether we know it or not."

The Odawa tribal chairperson agreed, "The Odawa and Ojibwe have lived in relationship to these dunes, water, plants, and animals for centuries, long before Europeans came along and divided the land and their trees and animals into bits and chunks, as if they were something you can buy or sell at the local dollar store."

Charity confirmed the papers for the lawsuit were delivered to O'Rourke at the company's local office and mailed to its headquarters in Delaware. When contacted, Mython Corporation's CEO Gale Mince had no comment. She referred the matter to the corporation's general counsel, Roscoe Rooter. "It's the company's property, plain and simple," Rooter said. "When you balance the loss against the huge social and economic benefits, like taxes and jobs and a new community on the shore that will replace the dune in thirty years, it's a win-win for all of us." He added, "We're confident the court will reject the injunction and dismiss the lawsuit. The claims are nothing but an illusion."

A courtroom showdown over the dune and the claimed mound has been assigned to Circuit Court Judge Odom "Odie" Holmes. His clerk, Dawn Nelson, said the court signed a temporary order halting any mining activities at the dune until the judge can hold a two-day hearing to decide whether the request for an injunction to stop the mining project should be granted.

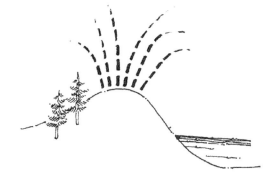

HISTORICAL NOTE

Recent anthropological and archaeological studies indicate that as long as five thousand years ago, people lived in the Great Lakes Region of North America near large mounds built in the shapes of panthers, water spirits, bears, and eagles. Some think these mounds are evidence of ancient villages and burial grounds. Others think that ancient people built the mounds to hold weeks-long ceremonies to restore harmony between the earth, sky, and spirit.

I t hadn't always been like this.

At one time, people's lives unfolded harmoniously here. People lived in small groups, roaming for food and shelter, migrating with the weather. Other groups settled, living off a variety of plentiful fish and berries, and growing plants that nurtured them. People lived along soft, embracing bays, and on long peninsulas that jutted into one of the inland seas in the heart of the continent.

The system of these large freshwater seas formed during the retreat of the glaciers at the end of the last Ice Age. For reasons unknown, the sun's energy that normally heated the planet had been redirected to other life forms in the galaxy. After many centuries, the other life forms healed, and the released energy returned to this planet. The planet's atmosphere warmed again, and as the glaciers melted and moved north, they gouged and sculpted high ridges, rolling hills, valleys, swamps, and gravel and sand plains.

It seemed as if it all happened by sacred agreement: a soft mixture of glowing emerald forests and meadows, white sands and blazing blue waters, stunning azure and floral-clouded skies. Vegetation exploded into vast forests of tall pines with elegantly long needles, hardwoods, berry bushes, and mushrooms. From above, a green blanket of undulating land surrounded the water, white sand beaches, and vast dunes along the shores. Fish moved in schools, leaping and gulping smaller fish and other aquatic food. Eagles, ospreys, and herons dove for fish, then soared in a dazzling white, blue-green light that illuminated an inner sense of radiance, soft and vulnerable, a tear in the corner of beauty's eye.

Harmony triumphed. Even today, despite the presence of a people long separated from this sense of vulnerability, a presence of this sacred agreement, an interlock of land and water, seems to remain, sending shivers down the spine and magical feelings into the hearts and minds of people who sit in silence long enough to be gladdened by it.

Recently, this interlock of land and water has been felt by those who have visited some of what anthropologists call animal-spirit mounds. Others claim blips have shown up on sound or electromagnetic field sensors used by ghost hunters. Notes from anthropologists who have studied the remnants of ancient people and their mounds record references to this phenomenon as Harmony Rays (HRs). They posit this in their studies of artifacts, the shape and location of the mounds, and these ancient cultures and their oral history. Although these so-called HRs have not been confirmed by reliable scientific instruments, tribal spiritual leaders acknowledge the presence in their people's relationship to the earth, especially a reverence for their ancestors and the mounds. Most people are unaware because they rely only on their rational mind, or what they're told to think by those with power over the machinery of civilization. After years and years of searching through molecules, atoms, electrons, protons, quarks, and charms, scientific maps point only to a void; this fact, if widely known, would reduce science to a box of information describing reality, not unlike other boxes of recent times, such as medicine, law, psychiatry, mathematics, economics, theology, and other intellectual systems. The void is given a scientific name so that it might have reality. But a few sensed no void at all, only what they referred to as "presence."

These so-called HRs permeated the Mound People's culture. Songs and dances carried the rhythm of the HRs—the few that have been deciphered attest to this: "wombing" described the act of giving birth to children; "nubbing" described a state of affection manifested by such acts as kissing, hugging, or rubbing against each other; what today might be called "godding" described a state of union with one and infinity. Beliefs didn't exist because reality simultaneously changed with their interaction of the HRs. Only the force of the HRs was described, and because this was dynamic, words and symbols were descriptive of an invisible dynamic nature, sometimes referred to as "beingness."

The Mound People traditionally honored these HRs on the longest, the shortest, and evenly balanced days of the planet's yearly cycle of light and dark. The Mound People traveled great distances to the large mounds that their ancestors formed to honor the spirit of the HRs. These mounds were always located near the shores of great lakes or, in some instances, near a waterfall or the rapids of a river. Some mounds were hundreds of feet high and a thousand feet long. They were shaped in the forms of the animals that lived in the region. Some were in the shape of bear, elk, or deer. Others were in the shape of foxes, wolves, raccoons, or beavers. The largest of these, which was near the geographical center of the others, seemed to be shaped like a panther. Anthropologists believe a panther mound represented a water spirit.

A Mound People's legend passed down through oral history tells of a story that these mounds absorbed the HRs of the region's land-water interlock. More than a dozen such mounds formed a path that spiraled outward from the panther mound. Because of the weakening of this interlock, the cause of which is unknown, those today who can still sense the HRs say they are now barely discernible.

The Mound People were invaded from time to time by hordes of hunters in search of food. When shifts in weather made it difficult for them to survive in their own lands, these hunters intruded on the region of other tribes. These ferocious hunters would slaughter their opposition.

The Mound People didn't need to hunt; what would normally be prey walked into their villages to offer themselves up. The invading hunters were so taken by the abundance of game they would follow game deep into the center of the lakes region. The Mound People let the invading hunters move freely, choosing not to reveal any sign of their presence, often hiding in the wooded hills. The invading hunters fell prey to a false sense of security—so much so that they became enchanted with the region and, over time, forgot where they came from. The HRs penetrated their beings, while the Mound People sat quietly watching them from behind the trees. When the invading hunters were overcome with the peaceful ambiance of HRs, they succumbed to sleep without guards or precautions.

Then the Mound People's strongest and most graceful leaders slipped silently through the night and captured the leaders of the invading hunters. The invading hunters woke in fear, not knowing what had happened to their leaders. When they looked about, they saw hundreds of Mound People, eyes peering at them from the pines. The hunters had been captured by something they could not see.

The Mound People gave those who wanted to leave food and guides to go back from where they came, never to return. Some would stay and live in camps for three Mound celebrations with tribes from distant lands, camping and joining in dances, games, trading, burying of the bones of the dead, and joining spiritual ceremonies. During this period, the HRs would transform the mind, body, and spirit of the invading hunters into Mound People. All traces of their invading heritage melted into the spirit of the Mound People. Time after time each wave of invading hunters would become fully absorbed into the blood of the Mound People. It is believed that while more ancient people preceded them, the Mound People's name is attributed to the Woodlands and Hopewell Indians who lived in the Upper Midwest one thousand years ago.

A recent news story reported that an old, scraggly-haired recluse claims there is a legend from the oral history of these ancient people who lived and built mounds along the shores of the inland seas of North America.

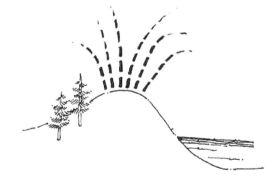

THE LEGEND OF MOLUV

… going, going, going to build mounds.

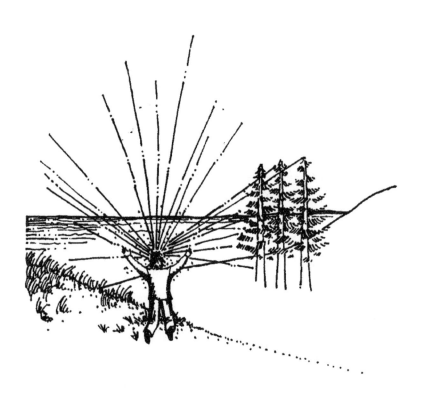

Moluv was a tribal leader of a band of Mound People who lived in the inland seas and upper river valleys of North America. It is thought they descended from an ancient people who lived in North America two or three thousand years ago, long before the Invading People came across the ocean from the east. While the Mound People did not have a chief in the sense of one leader, this band acknowledged the wisdom and gifts of several people in each generation. Some had auras or cascades of light around their bodies. Sometimes a gold-tinted white light shone from the center of Moluv's forehead and chest. He was an acknowledged traveler and seer. It was Moluv who sat quietly before great passages, giving directions as to what route to take for safe travel. It was Moluv and a select number of helpers who found and marked those lands that they envisioned would provide water, food, shelter, and protection from danger.

One night while on his back looking at the stars, Moluv received a sensation, a light breeze, then he heard a whisper. In the morning, he told his people: "We must move in the direction of the evening sun beyond the great waters."

Moluv gathered his guides, four men and two women known for their strength and prowess on water. They set out across the big waters toward the evening sun until they reached land; they would walk the distant shore, its woods, and its meadows, to find a new home. Moluv and other seers had been sensing a change within them and the land, its animals, and plants, for some time. They felt the center of the HRs shifting to the west, across the big water. To some, the West foretold their end. To others, like Moluv, it foretold a beginning.

The early morning sun warmed the backs of Moluv and his guides as they paddled past the last point of land. Moluv led in his canoe. The others followed in two larger canoes under the blue haze of the horizon. After paddling all day, Moluv and his guides approached the shore of a smaller peninsula. As they paddled closer, the dark, shadowy outline of the hills grew larger and larger. They had been paddling against a southwest headwind all day. Suddenly, the wind blew from the northwest. It blew hard. The waves of the lake swelled to heights as tall as the canoes were long. The guides angled their canoes into the waves so as not to be capsized.

The wind blew harder and harder; black thunderheads formed, darkening the sky. The rain slashed. It was cold. A bolt of lightning struck the water. Thunder and shocks of light surrounded them. They lost sight of any shore.

The waves swelled to greater heights, but Moluv led them onward. Not showing fear, he told his guides, "Look straight ahead, not at the waves."

Then another bolt of lightning tore at a wave behind them. The water foamed and sizzled, and a whitecap lashed out like the tongue of a snake, curling around the canoes, and swallowed them.

Everything was cold and turbulent. Moluv and the guides clung to the sides of the canoes as they rolled over and over in the darkness and force of the waves. They spun end to end, floated in air as they dropped to the trough, then shot upward as a wave met another sizzling bolt of lightning. Their pale-knuckled hands clung to the canoes, the force tearing at their arms; still they held on. The storm sucked them up and turned them end-on-end again. Then Moluv saw the youngest woman guide slip under the roiling, dark water. Her arm and hand pointed west, and she disappeared. Moluv climbed on the bottom of his canoe, his heart weeping as he fought to paddle with his hands in the direction of her arm. The black of night joined the raging storm. He fell unconscious.

The wind stilled. Smooth waves rolled evenly along the shore. A clear sky emerged out of the night. Dawn winked through orange-dusted clouds. Moluv felt his bruised body. His muscles ached. He lay there on top of his overturned canoe, looking for the other guides.

His heart ached. They were lost. He saw a point of land not more than a few hundred yards ahead. Hills covered with white pines rose behind the sandy shore.

The sun rose in the sky, heating his body and the sand share as one. He moved his arms and hands slowly through the water as the capsized canoe groped toward the shore. Through the clear waters he could see the sandy bottom several feet below him. When it was shallow enough to stand, he slid off the canoe to the welcome support of the lake bottom. He waded and dragged the canoe to the shore. After he pulled it up on the sand, he slumped to his knees. His brown skin looked black and blue from the bruises and the cold. He fell forward, holding his head in his hands, face first on the sand.

He began walking along the shore to the north of the sunrise. The shore kept curving in the same direction, and after a long while the sun was overhead, and he saw the canoe. He knew he was on an island.

His thoughts wandered, first going out to his guides. He worried about his people. He prayed to the sky spirit for them. He thanked the land and the water for carrying him to this unknown place. Falling into silence, his thoughts quieted and into the ache in his heart.

Then a voice startled him. "Lift up your head and see, Moluv. What has happened has happened." Moluv slowly lifted his head and looked around. There was no one there. Something tugged at him, and he rose to his feet and walked toward the crest of a ridge far above him. It was like a dream. He crawled up a steep slope of towering pines. Patterns of light danced on the mat of rust-colored needles. When he reached the ridge, he saw an opening, a meadow in the forest far below, and he continued to walk.

When he stepped into the meadow, he saw yellow, white, and purple wildflowers mingling with the vines of red and black berries. As he neared a patch of matted grass in the center of the meadow, a geyser of light shot up from the ground, and a shock wave knocked him to the ground. Dazed, he got up.

The light spoke. It was the voice again.

Moluv. Listen, listen, listen

Guiding, guiding, guiding
Coming, coming, coming
People. Invading, invading
Move, moving, moving.
Invading, destroying, invading …

Terrified, Moluv looked away from the dazzling light. He had experienced many visions, but none so frightening or mysterious. He was pulled back to the light. The voice spoke again.

Feeling, feeling, feeling
Energy shifting, shifting
Paddling, paddling, paddling
Far across the water
Energy sustaining, sustaining.
Water and sand creating
interlocking, interlocking
sky, land, and water
Centering, centering, centering
in mounds, mounding.
Energy weakening, weakening,
Forgetting, forgetting,
remaining, returning …
Going, going, going
Going to build mounds …

The light grew weaker, as he heard the voice whisper, "You must save our ways from the destruction that will come … The time is not for you to know. Go, now."

The voice faded. Only the wind murmured in the soft needles of the pines.

Transfixed, Moluv returned to his canoe and set off from the island once more. The wind fell to a whisper. A small white cloud appeared, and he paddled toward it until evening. He arrived in the shadows of hills, pulling his canoe from the shallows. He sat against a huge maple tree, and under the cover of its leaves and branches, he fell asleep.

He spent days walking the hills, ridges, marshes, and shores. He wandered up a valley and came to a steep dune that plummeted sharply to the inland sea. He knew then he had been guided by the light to this new land. He picked berries and shoots and put them in his canoe and paddled back to his people, in the direction from which he'd come.

His people greeted him with tight, worried faces. He told them what had happened to the guides. Mothers and fathers, sisters and brothers heaved with cries and sorrow. All of the people mourned, chanted, and danced for the loss of their dead.

Finally, they turned to Moluv and celebrated his return. Moluv showed them the shoots and berries, told them everything that had happened, then explained they must prepare for a long journey across the big water to the west.

After grieving and a full moon passed, in the calm of morning light, Moluv and his people left in large canoes filled with their belongings for their new land. Moluv could no longer remember. The meadow and geyser of white light—a distant dream. But he remembered his guides, their spirits given to the water for their people. And he remembered the message to go and build mounds.

When they arrived on the shore in the pink glow of their new hills and home, Moluv told his people of the message of the mounds. He led them to a valley and told them this was the place for their village and the mound. He led them up the valley to the top of the dune that dropped sharply to the shore. The graceful beauty in the folds of hills, vast waters, and the white dunes along the shoreline filled their hearts.

They built a large mound in the shape of a panther near a high dune close to their village that looked out over a vast inland sea. Over the years, other peoples near the shores and valleys of the inland seas and rivers built mounds. The different villages would send messengers, and their peoples would travel in the years that followed to celebrate the mounds and celebrate the unity of the sky and earth worlds. Centuries later, long after Moluv and his people passed into the sky of their Great Spirit, other people who settled the region discovered the mounds; they built their own mounds in other river and lake valleys. They didn't know why, only that their leaders knew that a visionary long ago had told their ancestors they must go and build mounds.

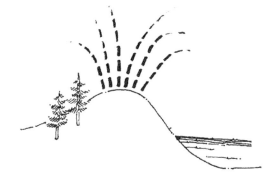

THE INVADING PEOPLE

... everyone wanted and expected to be a king or queen.

When the first Invading People arrived from across an ocean to the east a few hundred years ago, they came by way of long canoes and strange ships with large billowing sails. At first there were only a few of them, explorers looking for valuable metal ores and furs. They traded and lived with small bands of the Mound People. These first invaders became enthralled with the Mound People, and they told their friends across the ocean about the enchanted land to the west. Later, skilled adventurous missionaries brought teachings about God, who the Mound People knew as the one Great Spirit of the sky.

More and more people came trading irons-of-fire for the furs that found markets in the East. These irons-of-fire offered great control over others. They traded irons-of-fire for whatever they wanted. Never had the descendants of the Mound People seen such power. Surely, they thought, these Invading People must come from a sacred source, or they wouldn't be given such power. Then the Invading People brought woolens and drink that gave much pleasure. With the increased demand for furs, the animals with whom the Mound People had lived in agreement and unity for thousands of years dwindled in number. More Invading People came to the lakes, rivers, and forests. Some Mound People lost their way. Within a hundred years there were many more Invading People than Mound People. What Mound People were there lived in small, crowded settlements backed up against the shores of rivers and lakes.

These invaders had ridiculed the Mound People for their dances, drums, and other rituals, infected them and their children with illnesses, and claimed ownership of their land with their irons-of-fire. The Mound People didn't know what ownership meant; they only knew how puffed up the Invading People acted when they cleared trees, fished the streams and lakes, and built homes, with sheds, barns for horses and wagons, then stores and villages. The Invading People hurt or killed others in their obsession to own the land, the trees, and animals.

Soon, the Mound People lost their land, and they were forced to adopt the ways of the Invading People. Some stayed and continued to live in small bands on their land. Some thought they could keep their unity and favor with the HRs for the sake of the land, water, and their children. But many accepted these new ways and became separated from the land and their people. A few insulated themselves by living alone and away. But most joined the Invading People. Yet, no matter how hard they tried, deep inside they could never accept the invaders' ways. Some buried the loss of their pathways to wander, gather, and hunt in the pleasurable drink brought by the Invading People.

The Invading People spread their power and beliefs throughout the region of the inland seas and big rivers. These beliefs dated back several thousand years to another continent. This is another story but suffice it to say that by the time they inhabited what they believed was "their" land, their power and beliefs dominated and controlled much life on the continent they'd invaded—so they thought.

The Invading People glorified and worshiped their mind—their ultimate power. The Invading People believed that their religion gave them the right and power to dominate their new kingdom, It was ordained by their God. The mind, it was said, could by their will control and own every single "thing." They named plants, animals, lakes, rivers, and mountains after themselves as if they had "discovered" them. They collected them, mapped them, marked and surveyed them as if everything were theirs—forever to serve them. They reversed the flow of rivers, changed the levels of the lakes, and filled or emptied large areas of sponge-like swamps. Other land was cleared and hardened to connect towns and cities with roads. Long iron rails were placed next to each other to carry giant black steel engines that burned coal, spewed smoke, and pulled big wagons with wheels fixed to the iron rails to haul the trees to cities or to the ships that carried the fine trees back across the ocean.

Large buildings sprawled out and poked up everywhere. Tall stacks of fire spewed plumes that blanketed the cities. Then horse-less carriages carried people from the cities to the far reaches of the lake's region and beyond. Even more trees were cut and shipped near and far to build larger cities. Hills and mountains crumbled, some disappeared, under the grip of large machines. Machines burrowed deep into the earth to recover iron, copper, sand, clay, and gravel to make more machines, houses, buildings, horseless wagons. Men who worked for the governments formed by the Invading People adver-tised the land "for sale," selling it to others by handing them pieces of paper with the word "deed" or crafting words that declared it theirs. The Invading People used the deeds to push more and more Mound People off the land. They made even larger machines and irons-of-fire. Some machines flew like eagles and dropped balls of iron that fell to the earth, exploding with orange flashes of fire, some like the power of the sun destroying all life in their path.

Black oily liquid was pumped out of the ground to power the machines and horseless carriages that fouled the air and water. Black rock taken from the ground heated homes and boiled water to make steam that turned machines to generate electricity. This electricity traveled everywhere along wires. The electricity ran more machines. Some used an ore from the earth that exploded into great orange mushroom clouds of fire larger than the sun. Some machines flew like giant birds with trails of white vapor across the sky.

The Invading People passed laws that guaranteed to every person the right to be king or queen and control what was theirs—that is, if a person worked, collected enough pieces of paper currency to buy more power, things, and ideas, then these could never be taken away. Who did they dominate? Each other, whenever they could gain advantage. They called everything "resources"; even their own people were a "resource." They all wanted to be kings or queens, fed by the resources they took and owned.

The result of this kingship, this myth of royalty, was destruction (in their words, "progress"). Trees were not trees. Mountains were not mountains. Rivers were not rivers. Lakes were not lakes. Soil was not soil. Water was not water—all of it to serve, to be taken, owned, traded, or sold. Fish floated belly-up in muddy streams. Fish that didn't float belly-up were caught with the warning: "Don't eat the fish from these lakes; they contain chemicals that may be harmful to your health." Everything was a "resource."

> *It didn't matter water was taken from the lakes*
> *It didn't matter black oil covered the shore*
> *It didn't matter chemicals ruined drinking water*
> *It didn't matter if rain burned eyes or trees.*
> *It didn't matter if rivers turned into cement or dust*
> *or plumes of oil or green slime.*

The Invading People saw nature as doom hidden and lurking in dark shadows. Some said it was their sacred duty to subdue the enemy. They knew nothing of the spirit, nothing of harmony, the HRs in the land, water, and sky. Ironically, they were ignorant of the very force that sustained them, ignorant that they choked, strangled, cut, boiled, sucked, burned, boxed, and sold the very things on which their survival depended, the very things for which their encrusted hearts yearned.

Today many descendants of Invading People banded together, even joined by descendants of the Mound People, to fight to stop the corporations, demand their governments to restore the rivers and lakes, the marshes and forests, their towns and cities. They fought battles in streets and gray suits; their battlefields were darkly lit plastered rooms with cold white lights, long, smooth wood tables, and dark leather chairs, all of it far from the land and water they fought to cure. All of it to prove the "resources" taken to be owned and extracted were not good for the people and earth to fill their wants and desires. And even when these descendants won these battles, when they proved they were right, laws were passed to make wrongful extraction a "right"—because everyone dreamed, expected, and wanted to be a king or queen.

That mattered.

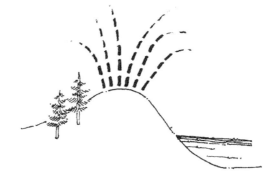

CORPORATIONS & ORGANIZATIONS

… fictional "persons"
made from words
chartered by their
rulers to do whatever
they please—take what
they want, spread
pleasure, drinks
with sweet chemicals,
pictures on screens,
big and flat on walls
or so tiny they
could hold them
in their hands …

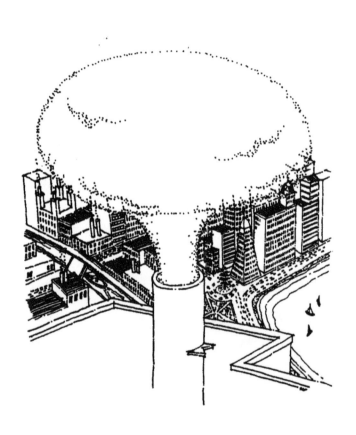

A global network of multinational institutions called corporations extended beyond and across the seas and land masses called continents. Toward the end of the twentieth one-hundred-year period from the birth of a divine presence (although they never understood Him and the spirit as more than a calendar, historical fact, or stained-glass window), these corporations controlled countries and states, and even religion.

If they didn't own countries, they would own natural resources—black oily stuff, combustible gases, uranium, coal, all kinds of land, and sand of a fine variety required for production of engines that ran their wagons and machines. To own or control the people in such countries, they gave them pleasure—drinks with sweet chemicals or pictures they would see on a flat gray object that lit up when plugged into or charged with electricity. Then they controlled words, images, and minds. Images passed invisibly through thousands and thousands of miles of cables, wires, and sky, and ran forever on screens big and small.

During these past ten years, people who had been crowded out or left behind with little to lose formed organizations to fight against their suffering or support each other to regain their power and control. They spoke out about devastating impacts on the air and water, the land and people, that all of this was causing. These groups formed organizations, large and small, international and local. They had one thing in common: each group sought to stop the waste, the poison, the disappearing of swamps, lakes, streams, the drying, dead soil, the fires, the floods, the hillsides sliding and killing because of rivers falling from the sky. Oddly, some of the people who complained about the pollution of their water in one place were often the same people who ran the corporations and polluted the air or water in other places. These elite few wouldn't acknowledge that their wealth and their resources had anything to do with the pollution and the destruction others screamed and raged about. Lifestyle? Control? Ownership? That mattered. So, the people who owned corporations without lungs or hearts continued to take, make, control, sell, and use whatever they needed to live their dreams to be kings and queens.

The Mython World Mining Corporation called a meeting of its Board of Directors at its headquarters in a distant city on the shore of an inland sea. The minutes of the meeting reflected the following:

MYTHON WORLD MINING CORPORATION, LTD. *Resource Extraction for Progress*

Minutes of a Meeting of the Board of Directors.
(Minutes in parenthesis are your recording secretary's)

The meeting was called to order by Chairperson Oliver Storm at 7:35 p.m. at the corporate headquarters. Board Secretary Richards asked for roll call:

Present: Dettmer, Hall, Norman, Pompton, Preston, Robb, and Connaghan, Richards, CEO Gale Mince, and executive staff.

Absent: R. Delp (fishing); J. Dempsey (hiking); M. Olsson (what's new).

Approval of the Minutes of last meeting. Approved with one revision: The last quarterly meeting was held in the offices of The World Mining Corporation Ltd. at the Rio Sands Desert Spa and Casino, Las Vegas, Nevada.

Environmental Insurance. After discussion concerning the discouragement of purchases of stock and bank financing because of the risk of liability for the harms the corporation caused, the board adopted a resolution to reimburse or indemnify officers, stockholders, and directors from any liability whatsoever arising out of their decisions or actions resulting in liability for injury, harm, or damage to others or the environment arising out of actions of the corporation. The resolution was adopted as follows:

Resolution No. 23-1313

WHEREAS Mython World Mining Corporation is a duly organized corporation with full rights of limited liability for any of its stockholders, protecting them from corporate actions which may cause damage, injury, or harm to property, persons, or the environment; and

WHEREAS there is increasing concern over whether insurance companies will insure against any damages from toxic, hazardous, or chemical liquid, substance, material, or combination thereof, contaminant or pollutant, greenhouse gases, or any other conduct resulting in impairment of the environment, water, air, wildlife, streams, wetlands, land, forests, or other unique and sensitive natural features; and

WHEREAS there is an increasing possibility that stockholders and directors may be sued and held liable for damaging the environment or people as a result of such contaminants or pollutants used in the course of, or as a result of, business dealings, corporate purposes or operations, due to the inventive practices of lawyers who represent such injured persons or the environment; and

WHEREAS the basic principle of a corporation is, and has always been, that stockholders, officers, and directors should be free from liability for injury or damage to others or the environment because or attributable to their decisions or actions made in the course of corporate ventures and affairs;

NOW THEREFORE it is resolved that any or all, or any number thereof, of the board of directors, officers, or stockholders of Mython World Mining Corporation Ltd. be and hereby are released and indemnified from any liability and indemnified for any damage or costs of any kind, including property, person, or environment, and attorney fees, that he, she, or they may incur, as the case may be, as a result of their decisions, actions, or inactions in pursuit of the business purposes and interests of the corporation for the benefit of its stockholders and officers.

The Voyager Dune Mining Project. After lunch, Chairperson Storm reopened the meeting and the board approved the consent agenda, and Mr. Richards announced the first matter of "old business"—the Voyager Point Sand Dune Mining Project:

Ms. Mince, would you present the problem?

Ms. Mince: Thank you, Mr. Storm. As you know from meetings over the past year, our Sands Corporation Division acquired several large parcels of land, 640 acres to be exact, one mile of shoreline along Lake Michigan to expand its sand mining operations in the region of the Great Lakes. The sand is well suited to industrial operations of other subsidiaries, as well as the automobile industry, the oil and gas industry for fracking shale development, and the steel industry. Until two months ago, plans and governmental approvals were routine. However, several conservation groups—a group called People of the Dune and a tribal group of Odawa, Ojibwa, and Potawatomi Indians (called the Mound People Coalition)—have filed letters and petitions opposing our mining permit from the Natural Resources Commission. The Mound People Coalition claims that there is something it calls a "sacred mound" under the dune. The primary basis of the objection is that mining will destroy a mound claimed to be historically and culturally unique. The People of the Dune claims that the project will destroy the geological and natural values of the dune that they claim are special and unique to the world. They claim the dune is important for habitat, recreation, and natural beauty. One letter, signed, anonymously, by a self-acclaimed psychic elder—more like a kook—says he's a descendant of some kind of ancient civilization, and said, to quote him, "There is a massive water spirit mound under the dune, and if it is destroyed by the mining, a spirit will be released on the world, and that will be the end of it as we know it." (whatever that means)

(Uproarious laughter from the Board)

Mr. Pompton: Maybe we ought to hire him.

(Laughter)

Mr. A. Robb: Sounds more like a Mark Twain character.

(Chuckles)

Mr. Preston: I've read where some of these indigenous people around the world think nature talks, like a lake, river, or mountain is a person or something, and that they are all part of their custom and culture.

Mr. Preston: Talk about legal fiction.

(More laughter)

At this point, a gravelly voice came from the audience of stockholders. It came from a thin, wiry, long, scraggly, white-haired old man, unshaven and dressed in bib-overall jeans and a dark green shirt with yellow daisies. No one knew how he got into the room. He said his name was "Solon Creek," and that he was the one who wrote the letter to the Natural Resources Commission. Chairperson Storm asked him to leave. He refused, so, security started to remove him. He pulled out a certificate for one share of Mython World Mining Corporation stock, claimed he was a descendant of a leader of ancient people who lived in the middle of North America several thousand years ago. Then he said, "I'm warning you on behalf of the mound, you'll start the end days of your corporation," and he kept repeating, "There is a mound buried under the dune. Do not mine. Do not mine." The chairperson politely offered the man a chance to add anything that might be of help, but to refrain from such falsehoods and emotional outbursts. The old man left, shaking his head, murmuring, "Beware, the mound is earth, sky, and spirit. Your end is near."

Secretary's Note: Our corporate security division has since confirmed that the man, Solon Creek (we haven't found any birth record, address, driver's license, bank account, Social Security number, nothing) lives in a shack at the base of the dune, and that there are now these groups, the Mound People Coalition and People of the Dune, who have put up tents, temporary toilets, cooking facilities, a stage for entertainment—it is already a de facto village of more than seventy people; we're worried it will grow and get out of our control and interfere with our schedule to commence mining. I've referred this to our legal counsel for possible eviction.

After a recess, discussion on the Voyager Dune Mining Project resumed.

Mr. Richards: This Creek fellow sounds like a nut, a self-acclaimed psychic recluse who has no documented identity. In his letter to the Natural Resources Commission, he stated he has lived in a cabin most of his life. I don't think there's anything we need to worry about. If the place were sacred, you'd never know it from looking at him.

(Chuckles)

CEO Ms. Mince: Please, Mr. Richards, would you please get to our strategy before the commission?

Mr. Richards: We are going to do two things. First, we have donated a total of $250,000.00 for assistance in the past three months to some influential environmental organizations, donations to unnamed elected officials' campaign funds, and a village park near the dune. We expect they will offer and support changes in our mining operation to lessen pollution, but not oppose it. We do not intend to buy influence, of course, but to help them in their work of reviewing our operations' effects on the environment. Second, we will introduce a series of visually pleasing overlay maps, depicting what the one-square mile mined area will look like after the twenty-year mining phase. It's done by Nature's Designs, Inc., the country's leading resort design firm. It will show a destination resort of lakes, marinas, golf courses, a hotel, an observation tower two hundred feet in the air, homes, stables, gardens, trails, and a spa to be located on the land that is not mined. Homes and condominiums will be located in four fine residential villages of three hundred homes each with water and sewer infrastructure. The drawings are so pleasing, it'll be hard to say the result of the mining has harmed or impaired the environment and land that remains. In fact, it'll be an improvement. While the mound may be gone, what's in its place will be an example of a harmonious human use and increase of needed jobs and tax base for the rural area. Very aesthetic.

(PowerPoint maps and drawings popped up one after the other as the board ogled the presentation by the project director for Nature's Designs.)

Mr. C. Connaghan: Win-Win for everyone, including money for Mython's stockholders. The area looks beautiful, particularly the wooded hills and beaches along the lake. Tell the development division to send me some information.

Mr. Richards: Yes, in the long run, our resort project will generate more money than the mining.

Mr. A. Robb: What about the chemicals? Any possibility of contamination?

Mr. Richards: I'll defer to Mr. Trustin from staff.

Mr. T. Trustin: There should be no contamination of the groundwater by the additive solution used in the process for washing the sand. There's a creek nearby, and some excess water will be discharged into it from the operation so that it doesn't dry up. The detectable levels do not exceed the naturally occurring background levels of metals and should not upset water quality.

Mr. Hall: And is there a backup plan on this?

Mr. Robb: Don't count on environmental insurance with all these global warming catastrophes.

Mr. Trustin: We've got other additives we can use that have been developed by our chemical division, a fifth-generation chemical, the compound structure of which is a protected trade secret and designed so it cannot be detected by any of the government's lab technology. At least none that we know of.

Mr. A. Robb: Cat and mouse, one step ahead of the cat.

(Chuckles)

Mr. Pompton: What about evicting these intruders and this illegal tent village?

CEO Mince: We're waiting to hear from legal counsel. We don't want to take any action that would upset our position and good faith toward the larger community in the court case that has been filed. Once we get the "green light," we can deal with the trespass.

On Motion of Hall and second from Dettmer, the meeting adjourned at 10:47 p.m.

(The Board retreated to the Vista Room for mint tea and bottles of Cinsaut reds, and a catered Moroccan dinner of ribs and rice.)

Six weeks after the Mython World Mining Corporation's Board of Directors' Meeting, there was another meeting, this one attended by a coalition of nonprofit corporations, tribes, and people who vowed to stop the mining of Voyager Dune. A copy of the minutes of their meeting revealed the following:

FIRST MEETING OF THE PEOPLE OF THE DUNE and THE MOUND PEOPLE COALITION

Minutes by Ann Look. We called the meeting to order on the shore of Lake Michigan, 6:00 p.m. The following groups and organizations were there:

Bay Ecology Council, Jane Tibbins, Ray Conner, legal counsel

Sand Mound Conservation Group, Ann Look; Desert Wilderness Society, Phil Dilley

Mound People Coalition, Buster Chippewa, chair, Benjamin Rastellar, legal counsel

Love Locally, Love Globally Group

People of the Dune, Chelsea Charity, coordinator, Griz Haynes, legal counsel

Others present:

Sam and Stuart Jorgenson, Jake Kellum, Jane Tibbitts, Mary Williams, Amos Yoder, David Davidson, Paul and Sunny Hunt, Jay Jones, "Doc" Hall, Trudy Swier, Rusty Bates, Steve Rochan, Richard Doyle, Patricia Case, and an older skinny man, Solon Creek, with thin face, bird-like nose and white hair, worn wool pants, T-shirt and leather vest, claiming to represent the ancient Mound People. He said he lives in a shack up a ravine on the backside of the dune, that he's a descendant and knows some of the oral history of the ancient people who built sacred mounds. He said there's a mound buried under the dune, that he speaks for his ancestors and someone he called Moluv, who led these ancient people over two thousand years ago.

The group sat in a circle around a campfire to encourage consensus. Chelsea Charity was nominated to facilitate the discussion. Everyone gave a statement explaining why they were at the meeting. Ray Conner stated that his group opposed mining because of its rare geological features, stating that there was nothing like the Voyager Dune in all of the world. Ann Look said she had lived in the Bay Region for ten years, and that she believed the dune shouldn't be mined because of the enjoyment it brought to so many who picnicked there. She also said that there were plenty of places to mine sand and that mining the dune wasn't necessary. Phil Dilley, a lawyer, said that after several camping experiences on the dune, he personally had become attached to it, and didn't want it tampered with. Jake Kellum, who explained the plant life on the dune, said mining would destroy irreplaceable endangered plants. He also said the dune shouldn't be altered because, "That's the way it was before I was born, and I'd like to see at least something in my life pass on to my grandchildren in the same condition."

There were cheers of "right-on." Others expressed agreement and said they "just wanted to give good energy to everyone." Then, the older, thin man said, "You can't mine the mound. It'll be the end. Put your faith in the mound. I have felt its presence as a grace for a long time." Everyone tried to ask him what he meant, but he shrugged it off and left, mumbling something like, "Beware … mmm … the mound's sacred."

Charity walked over and told him he could stay and just listen if he wanted. He said, "I've got to get back to my house, my mound." She gave him a hug. His shoulders stiffened as if he hadn't been hugged in a long time, then he broke into a toothless smile.

Everyone sat quietly until Charity finally opened the session to discuss strategy.

Paul Hunt: I think we should go to the commission and object without compromise. If the company won't back off—and they probably won't—someone should take it to court.

Sunny Hunt: Well, maybe the company will see the light. I think if we all hold hands, we can forget this negativity. Just imagine the company people not showing up at the commission. Just send them love so that they do the right thing. It's got nothing to do with fights and fists.

Conner: Come on. We must prepare for a court case. That's the system. Enough superstition.

Sunny Hunt: Since when is love superstitious?

Charity: We've gotten a little off base. Couldn't we go through the commission, then decide if we should go to court? And, if we go to court, this idea of Sunny's is a good one. We can pack the courtroom, a whole bunch of us, sit on the floor, and send out positive energy to the judge.

Rastellar: You'll need to advise the court ahead of time, so the judge and his staff aren't caught off guard. No surprises. It'll be difficult as it is.

Yoder: You know, the courtroom's just another place to fight. Word-swords. It's all adversarial, word-fist, expensive. Why can't we just protest and stop this land-ripping company? We all know the drill. Lay limp in front of the machines, let them arrest and drag us away, burden the system every damn day until they get the message.

Rastellar: That might stop the company for a day or two until you're arrested. It won't expose the underlying sacred nature of what we think is buried under the moving sands of the dune. We have three branches of government, and one of them is the courts.

Yoder: Well, I say there's a fourth branch—people.

Charity: Amen, Amos, you've got a point, but maybe our protest and presence in the courtroom will get the attention of the judge's mind and heart.

Williams: Charity, why are you always so naive?

Charity: What's wrong with that?

Williams: Fat chance. I'm with Amos. I think we should protest and stop the mining. I'm going right now.

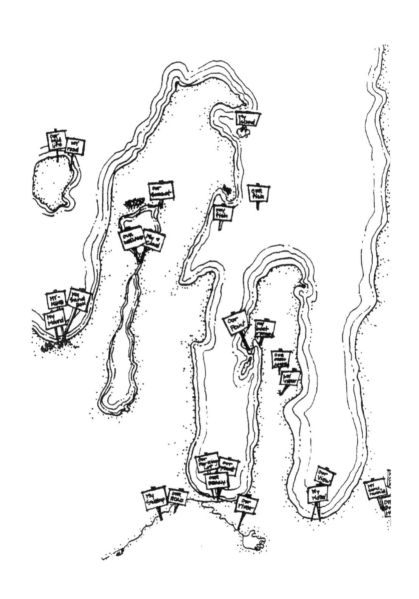

Tibbins: Well, what about a lawsuit? Can the company sue us for lots of money for bringing the suit?

Conner: You can't stop anyone from suing anyone in this country.

Dilley: Are you kidding? They bought the land for practically nothing when you look at the profits they'll make. There's nothing in it for them to back down.

Conner: But what does that do? You protest, get arrested, and all the while the police and courts help the company at the cost of taxpayers.

Charity: We need to prepare to go to court, but we need lots of groups to join in. How are we going to pay the lawyers their fees, that's the question. And the expert witness fees on top of those.

Look: Barter.

Rastellar: I can represent the tribe, but you'll have to get a lawyer, and bartering with a lawyer, that's like trying to bargain with someone who doesn't need what you have to offer.

Tribal chair Chippewa: A yearly supply of white fish? Who wouldn't take that?

(Laughter)

There was more talk about the high cost of lawyers and doing it without any. But an agreement was reached: lawyers are an unavoidable necessity.

Williams: Frankly, I think I'm changing my mind. Protest and arrest may make the most sense for some of us.

Rastellar: If some want to protest, fine. But I wouldn't put all your faith in it.

Kellum: Well, I'm not sure about going to court either when the enemy's got all the power.

Charity: A protest with love might be okay, but only if we've tried to communicate in the courts first.

Williams: But if we act like pansies, they'll run over us like pansies. I'm leaving …

(Mary left the room, Amos, David, Sunny, and Ann went with her)

Conner: The courtroom is a protest, but we'll appeal to their game of science and intellect.

Kellum: I'd like to, mister. But that's not going to stop them.

Tibbins: So, if we go to court, does that mean they can sue us, too?

Conner: Not if we form a nonprofit corporation that limits personal liability of stockholders.

Dilley: Yes, but individuals can still be held personally liable in events of bad faith or recklessness. But you can include in the bylaws a provision to defend and indemnify any member, director, or officer if they're sued.

Tibbins: Assuming you have the money to do that.

Conner: There's insurance for officers, directors, and members.

At this point, the minutes show a lengthy discussion about using a not-for-profit corporate form to organize, collect funds to fight the case, and acquire insurance to protect everyone from liability. Then, those at the meeting adopted the following:

Charity: I call for a vote.

All but Jake Kellum voted in favor.

Kellum: If we've got a good case, why fear getting sued? They aren't going to interfere with my right to redress a wrong.

The resolution stated:

All of the corporate entities who form any party of a coalition to bring any court or other action against any person or corporation or the government to prevent and stop mining of the dune shall release any director, officer, or member of any personal liability, and shall indemnify such person or persons in the event they are held personally liable for their actions or conduct.

No consensus was reached, but everyone decided to try and support the action of each other. The meeting closed with a silent cheer for the Voyager Dune and the mysterious mound.

(All adjourned for delicious banana cream tofu pie. The pie was mmm heavenly, still wondering what the scraggly man was talking about.)

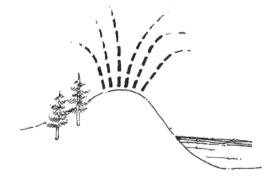

A CAMP-IN & LAWSUIT

"But what would happen to the dune? Is the dune sacred? Just who owns the dune? Is there a mound? Is it sacred? Who owns the mound?"

These were the questions ...

The daily headlines continued to flash messages of destruction and pollution—conflicts over "My this" or "My that," "Ours this" or "Ours that," never ended. Nothing ever seemed to get resolved.

Much concern emerged about the inland seas region because of a "national" energy policy that eyed the lakes as a source for the massive amounts of water required for drinking, food, to convert the mountains in the west to black oily liquid for machines and what they call cars and trucks, vehicles of all kinds, and to generate electricity. They drained lakes and rivers, the waters under the ground, until it looked like towing icebergs offered a better option, and then they fought over who owned the water and the icebergs. But something else appeared in the papers—not on the front page, not in large print, but once again in the local "news briefs" section.

The coalitions and groups that opposed the mining gained little notoriety in the papers or what is known as social media. But on a dry August afternoon, thigh-high dune grass lifeless in the hot sun, some of their members decided to quietly camp near the end of the entrance road at the foot of the dune. More and more tents popped up by evening. By dusk, the smoke from the glowing embers of a row of campfires mixed with the warm air and pinkish-gray striated clouds in the sky. Campers put up signs along the road: Sacred Mound. Living Dunes, Stay Out. Men, women, and children sat quietly for hours. Soft talk, laughter. Then drums and singing. They danced. They sat. They drank. They ate. They slept. They kept watch all night. By dawn the number of tents had doubled. The sunrise to the east turned the tents into a rainbow of colors.

The Mython World Mining Corporation's board of directors called an emergency meeting with their top officials in a resort on a lake several miles south of the dune. The company's executives hadn't figured on an occupation by these people. They knew they could handle the many citizen groups, nearby property owners, and government, but they didn't know what to do with the tent city that spread out between the country road and the dune.

"What rights do these people have?" the executives asked their lawyers.

"As you can see by our report, none that we know of. They're trespassing," they responded.

"Well, then, let's get a court order and kick them the hell out of there; they're on our property," the chairperson ordered.

The next day, their lawyers got a magistrate's order, and the local sheriff's department and a squadron of state police cars turned onto the entrance road, dust following them to the camp. Two deputies, automatic weapons in their arms, along with a man holding a stake and sledgehammer, escorted a uniformed man, who delivered the order to the campers. The man with the stake pounded it into the ground, pulled out a staple gun, and fastened a copy of the order to the stake, which read EVICTION NOTICE in red letters.

After the process server left, the sheriff and police squadron waited and waited for the campers to leave. But no one moved. The campers pulled out the posts, taunted the guards, and tossed notices into campfires. By afternoon, more than fifty campers had been hauled away in vans to the local jail to appear before a magistrate the next morning.

Seven men and three women were formally arraigned on trespass and other charges. The rest of the campers were released. Solon Creek was also arraigned. When asked by the magistrate whether he would plead not guilty or guilty, he said, resolutely, "I have lived in my shack on the land for more than sixty years. I have rights by what you call adverse possession. I'd call it squatter's rights. There's something more at the dunes than rights." The magistrate looked inquisitively at the prosecutor for a response. Nothing. Then she asked Creek what he meant.

"My ancestors lived there for centuries, every generation down to me. My parents died when I turned fourteen, so I built my shack in the grove of maples on the eastern slope of the dune, next to the area where I have felt that there's a sacred mound buried under the dune. I feel like one of them. I don't know who they were, but something happened there." The magistrate peered over her reading glasses at the prosecutor again, begging him for a response. "Mr. Wooster, I don't think the court wants to hear an adverse possession lawsuit in a criminal proceeding," the magistrate said. The prosecutor, befuddled, dismissed the charges against Mr. Creek.

The magistrate turned to the remaining bedraggled campers, calling themselves the "Voyager Dune Ten," and set bail for their release at $1,000.00. A woman who owned a nearby centennial cherry and hog farm stepped forward and posted bail.

The news media picked up the story. Headlines read, "Tribes Claim Dune Is Sacred," "Protesters Jailed for Trespass, Obstruction of Justice, and Breach of Peace." Another front-page headline and story read:

MINING COMPANY TO BEGIN MINING LAKESHORE'S DUNES

City-on-the-Bay, Michigan. MYTHON, one of the world's largest natural resource mining corporations, has announced that it has acquired lease rights and permits to the Voyager Point Sand Dune, and that it will start mining the sand for its industrial processes in two weeks. The Natural Resources Commission approved the permit last week in an emergency session over the cries of busloads of protesters. Environmental groups threatened to file suits to protect the mound, because it is a unique and rare resource not found anywhere else on the globe. They claim it has rare vegetation, contours, and is valuable for recreation and scientific study. Groups calling themselves People of the Dune and the Mound People Coalition have set up an encampment of tents near the base of the Voyager Point Dune.

Nearby property owners have also threatened legal action because the mining will cause traffic, dust, noise, and reduced property values. But the Council of Commerce says it supports Mython World Mining Corporation, because the County needs the jobs and taxes. The auto industry says it will do whatever it must to back the mining, claiming it is necessary for the casting of engines. The oil and gas industry claims the sand is needed to mix with liquefied high-pressured fluids used to break the bones of shale formations two miles below the ground. The Department of Commerce claims that the unemployment and condition of the state's economy is so fragile that the state cannot afford to oppose mining regardless of environmental impacts.

The governor's office refuses to comment.

Follow this story at www.city-on-the-bay.com/news/dune/mining.

The next day, people from everywhere, protesting the plight of the "Voyager Dune Ten," showed up at the foot of the dune. So many people had set up tents, they set up a sign, dubbing the camp "Dune Village." Its population ballooned to over two thousand, with food trucks, water tankers, porta-johns, and beer tents. The technicians from a summer music festival called Bliss showed up and set up a stage and sound system. Protesters surrounded Mython's corporate prefabricated office and maintenance garage to the pounding beat of a bodhran from an Irish folk band. Fifty armed Pinkerton guards cordoned off the entrance road and turned back any newcomers. So, a large number of newcomers set up camp in a pasture opposite the entrance road and posted signs that read "East Dune Village."

"Let's hear it for the Voyager Dune. The sacred mound!" cheered a translucent-eyed coed.

"Better than Woodstock," quipped a middle-aged, bald and

bearded man in a light blue T-shirt with a hand-painted yellow dune on the front.

A week later, after the corporation announced it would begin mining, the People of the Dune and Mound People Coalition, representing the tribes, and a man named Solon Creek filed lawsuits to stop the mining of the dune and protect the supposed, mysterious sacred mound. Soon after, the Bay Ecology Council sought to intervene to protect the dune's habitat and the creek. Another organization, the International Society to Preserve Indigenous Lands, also sought intervention, because local tribal people had become members. The Social Justice Committee for People of Color joined the Indigenous Lands group. The International Rights of Nature Coalition joined, claiming the Voyager Dune has the rights of a person, or living being, that cannot be violated or invaded. A Society for the Esoteric Study of Spirit Mounds and Eschatological Study of Last Things jointly sought to intervene, claiming the mining would destroy their ability to learn what the mounds of sand might mean for the future of humankind. There was even a group calling itself the Society of International Ologists, whose members offered opinions and integrative studies on everything. The Dune Mobile Association filed suit, claiming the mining would ruin a potential area for their recreational dune buggies. The Energy Alternative Group joined the suits, claiming that the dune's pinnacle was more valuable for wind turbines to produce renewable energy. The Mound Area Homeowners Council, who represented those who lived nearby, intervened, claiming damages for the nuisance and loss of value to their property. Even the local government where the mound was located joined the homeowners' groups to recover loss of property tax revenues because the state government granted Mython a ten-year real property tax exemption. And the local chapter of the Desert Wilderness Society intervened, claiming that the mining would destroy the most unique area for desert wilderness camping experiences west of the Kalahari.

Mython World Mining Corporation denied the claims, spouting that the lawsuits were "spurious," "unwarranted," and other legal jargon. Corporate officials flooded social media and showered brochures on the community, assuring everyone that the public welfare of the state required the mining, and that there was no alternative to mining the dune because the sand is on the land where nature left it. Industries who needed the sand, and trade and commerce groups joined the suit on behalf of the defendant corporation, principally the World Trade Mining Organization, the National Mineral Institute, and the Chamber of Business and Industry. The International Fund for Economic Development filed written arguments in support of the defendant Mython, claiming to be a "friend of the court."

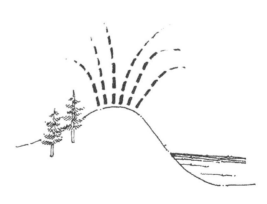

THE
HEARING

*"We've been
living here
for twelve thousand
years."*

The court hearing began almost two weeks after the newspaper article reported the date the mining of the dune would begin. Three days before the hearing, the organizations that brought the lawsuit met to map out a strategy if they would lose. After several hours of disagreement over civil disobedience and justified criminal disruption, they decided to defy any court order or action that allowed the company to mine.

As the hearing began, trial judge Odom Holmes came out of his office chambers behind the court's bench, carrying a book in one hand and a hammered-bronze, table-sized sculpture of Lady Justice with scales, sword, and blindfold in the other, which he placed next to him on the top of the bench. The court clerk placed a stack of files and documents on his desk high enough to hide behind. Judge Holmes winced when he looked beyond the oak railing, where a retinue of twenty-three lawyers, experts, and assistants sat crowded around two long counselor tables. A crowd packed the courtroom, spilling into the corridor. The July heat was sweltering. Foreheads and pipes sweated. Air conditioning vents roared with cold air.

When Judge Holmes opened the top file from the stack next to him, he saw the two pages of lawyers and law firms who had filed papers in the case. *Maybe I should move the mob to the high school gym,* he thought. *Not enough bathrooms for the lawyers, let alone the crowd. Damn county commission hasn't forked over the money to update this hundred-year-old icon of a building since the 1960s. If I can figure out which lawyer goes with which client or party, I'll be on my way to finishing in two months.* This was not something he relished doing during the sweet-spot days of summer. Luckily, his clerk began placing lawyer-client name tags on the front of the suitcoat of each lawyer. Boxes of files, laptops and power cords, yellow pads of paper and pens filled the tables and sprawled on the carpeted floor.

"I've read your written arguments," the judge said. "I'm not wasting a day listening to a couple of dozen opening statements. Save your arguments after we've heard all of the evidence. Let's get to it."

Expert witnesses of all types, from a hydrologist (groundwater) and soils mechanic (sand-slope stability) to an expert on sandpipers, killdeer, and mound thistle, took the stand. It was clear that the mining would destroy the Voyager Dune. Then, an archaeologist and anthropologist testified about the tens of thousands of mounds built by tribes who settled the Great Lakes, and the Ohio and Mississippi River basins, thousands of years ago. Another acclaimed anthropologist, called as a witness by the tribes, said many of the large mounds along rivers and lakeshores were sacred, that they reached so far back in time that they may well represent the lost culture of the original people in the region of the inland seas and rivers. Indigenous, he said. He also said that the sacred mounds restored harmony between the earth and Great Spirit in the sky. An economist offered that the mining was not necessary because of decreasing demand. An expert in eschatology, who was also a member of what is called the Society of Ologists, offered an opinion on the meaning of the dune as it related to the meaning of everything, launching Mython's lawyer to his feet with a string of objections to relevancy. "If it's related to everything, how can it not be relevant?!" the ologist said. Judge Holmes politely said, "Well I'll accept your testimony for what it's worth, but it may be too broad to have any meaning."

Defendant Mython's lawyer argued that the legislature had passed the mining law with the intent to encourage mining, that "Necessarily, your Honor, the law was never intended to stop the mining of Voyager Dune. My client can only mine this valuable fine sand where it finds it. The law only protects the resources and environment that remains."

"Excuse me, your Honor," the People of the Dune's lawyer said. "But if the law protects only what remains, nothing will remain until the last dune or lake is gone!"

"I object, your Honor. My client holds the exclusive right of extraction and production of the fruits of the land." Then the company's own economists calculated the overwhelming value for private profits from the company's property—four billion dollars, he testified—and that there were benefits to the state and community for industry, jobs, and taxes, all with their projected multiplier effects. Then, an international development firm's chief executive explained how the end-value of the dune and nearby property and the village would be more valuable for the good of everyone than the dune itself: he said that the leveled dune would be reclaimed as beautiful artificial lakes and high-class residential development; there would be no impact on what remained. Indeed, what remains will enhance the value of residences in the area and quality of the region's environment. Another one of the company's first-string lawyers piped up, "These benefits are far more essential to the general welfare of all citizens in the state, not just these people who want it to sit there and enjoy the view," which sparked a wave of protestations and prompted Judge Holmes's reproof to everyone in the courtroom: "Please, remember the ground rules."

Plaintiffs countered with many things: that the dunes, particularly the Voyager Dune and its plants and animals and lakeshore, were natural marvels, unique to the world; the real value, as they put it, is the dune as a dune. It must be preserved, they claimed, because it has the right to be protected in the same manner as a person is protected from bodily harm. An environmental psychologist testified that over the past hundred and fifty years, those who live along or near the dune have become so connected to the dune that it is inseparable from their well-being. The tribes' historian addressed the value of the mound—its cultural-historical significance: "Our people don't have a word for property," he testified. "We live in relationship with the trees, the water, and the animals; the mound and the dunes, too. These dunes have been living here long before the Great Spirit placed our ancestors here."

Then the historian for indigenous people around the world opined, "There is a deep relationship of the tribes to these land formations, which if severed by the mining would violate their cultural rights." Other experts went on to show that chemically laced discharges would pollute the groundwater, removal of the dune would alter the currents and erosion patterns of the large lake, and rare vegetation like puccoon and populations of killdeer and endangered piping plover would be lost. An economist then testified that the tourist-based economy and recreational values were incomparable in value and character. An expert from the International Union for the Conservation of Nature testified that a nearby national lakeshore park would be severely altered, and that removal of the Voyager Dune would break the continuity of these three-hundred-mile world-class coastal dunes.

A woman wearing dark pants, silk blouse, and blazer—one of a long line of corporate lawyers sitting at lawyer's tables on the defense side of the courtroom who looked like a choir in their dark suits and white shirts—stood up waving a certified copy of defendant's Exhibit 1, the company's warranty deed, "I object, your honor! All this evidence is completely subjective and immaterial to my client's undisputed ownership rights. This case is not about good and evil, it's about our deed, title, and exclusive rights to this land and what we can do. I ask the court to strike this testimony from the evidence."

Judge Odom Holmes began ruminating. *The mining company's private property for its own use and profit? The many people represented by the plaintiffs for their leisure and enjoyment. No one? Who? A relationship between people and nature. Didn't that count for something? The loss of the mound a potential cultural genocide? The gap in the dune an identity crisis, a gap or blind spot in human nature or the mind?*

Judge Holmes unknowingly put his hand on Lady Justice's blindfold and gazed back at the long train of lawyers. "Well, I'm going to allow all of the testimony, and give it the weight it is worth. If it's not worth much, I won't give it much. On the other hand, I would rather see all the evidence, hear all the evidence, on the chance it may help me see better to decide what I have to decide today."

The tribe's lawyer, Rastellar, stood up and spoke. "Your honor, it's our position, among others, that you must look at how my clients' ancestors viewed the land, water, plants, and trees … to the point, the mound itself, long before what we know as property law ever existed. My clients' relationship with the land preexists the Treaty of

1836 that ceded ownership of the land. Nowhere in the treaty did they cede their cultural relationship to the land, the water, the plants, and the animals. If this relationship was not, and we think could not be, expressly conveyed, then my clients' ancient perceptions, cultural relationships, including uses that are part of that relationship, remain intact. Their right to fish, hunt, and gather is strong evidence of the tribal relationship to the land. Thus, any right to continue their relationship to the mound is theirs, a right in the tribe, not the individual, which existed long before any federal government patent conveyed title of surveyed boundaries and property to the first property settlers in this region in the mid-1800s. Therefore, your Honor, these rights could not and were not conveyed by any of the subsequent deeds, including the exhibit showing the defendant's property boundaries and title up to this day."

A loud roar and applause broke out in the courtroom. Judge Holmes raised his hand for quiet.

"Nada … Nada … there are no court decisions in western civilization, the United States, let alone this state, your honor, which support this argument," the mining company's lawyer retorted.

"These mounds are … this mound is like a song that comes from our history, our very existence," the tribal lawyer said. "The history of ownership of title in the register of deeds' office runs back a mere seventy years. Our people's presence as a tribe runs back a thousand years, and generations of ancestors before them point back ten thousand years, back into the mystery of their origin story."

"Well, your Honor, Mr. Rastellar makes an interesting argument, but what he's saying would nullify every recorded real estate title or title insurance policy in this state," the female lawyer in the blazer and silk blouse said. "The real problem is that there's no evidence that this alleged mound exists at all."

The People of the Dune's lawyer Griz Haynes sprang from his seat and faced the bench. "Your Honor, may I speak?" There being no response from the judge, he said, "There is a long line of cases right up to the Supreme Court's Illinois Central decision in 1892 declaring the Great Lakes off limits for development …"

"Your honor, the Illinois Central case has nothing to do with dunes, it's about water," the woman lawyer said.

"A careful reading of the decision shows that the Supreme Court opened the door for a court to protect upland property of a special character from impairment," lawyer Haynes replied. "If you find this to be the law, well, then this case should go to trial, and you should issue an injunction to protect the status quo of the dune until there's a final decision."

"You're asking me to extend a doctrine that protects water to land? How am I supposed to do that?" a brow-troubled Judge Holmes said, then glanced at the clerk and called for a recess.

"Counsel … I mean all of the attorneys and clients in this matter. You can wait here, or you can check in with the clerk's office. I realize time is critical to all of you, so, come hell or high water—strike that. That's not the best choice of idiom these days … I intend to issue an opinion from this bench today, no matter what."

(Court Reporter's Note: Judge Odom Holmes picked up an armful of files and papers and retreated through a large oak door to his chambers.)

After what seemed days, the gold-plated knob on the oak door to the judge's office turned, and the bailiff bellowed, "All rise, the Honorable Odom Holmes presiding." The judge's footsteps echoed throughout the courtroom as he climbed the oak steps to his seat on the bench. He slid the papers from one arm onto the bench, and placed the books cradled in his other arm on the bench in front of him. He looked up at the standing-room only courtroom; he stared at the blur of dark suits and white shirts—some with Windsor-knot ties, others with open collar and gold necklaces—standing at attention behind the counselor tables. He paused and studied the sculpture of Lady Justice sitting on the bench next to him and nodded at his clerk who decorously announced: "The case of *People of the Dune, Mound People Coalition et al. versus Mython World Mining Corporation*, Case Number 23-77-01 CE, is back in session."

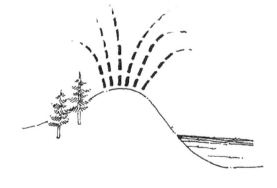

EXCERPTS FROM THE BENCH OPINION & ORDER OF JUDGE ODOM HOLMES

Is there any law, constitution, or common law court decision that limits the property right to mine because of the common, unique nature of the Voyager Dune ... ?

HONORABLE ODOM RANDOLPH HOLMES, CIRCUIT COURT JUDGE, PRESIDING.

(Back on the record, 9:17 p.m.)

Judge Holmes: Thank you for your patience. Given the range of claims and arguments over the Voyager Point Dune, I am tempted to adjourn for a week. However, mindful of the importance of this to all of you, the divergent views, the emotions, and tensions here, and at what now appears to be a growing camp-in at the base of the dune, I have decided to state my opinion on the record in open court today, right now. I expect everyone in the courtroom to remain pin-drop quiet until I have finished.

*   *   *

So, there are two motions, requests for rulings, for me to decide. First, plaintiffs, Mound People Coalition, Mr. Creek, and People of the Dune, joined by others, ask me to grant them an injunction to halt any activity by defendant to mine the dune. When plaintiffs filed their lawsuits, I granted only a temporary order, stopping the defendant corporation from mining until I could hold this hearing. Second, the defendant, Mython Corporation, asks me to dismiss the case entirely because the law does not embrace plaintiffs' claims.

For me to grant the injunction, the plaintiffs must prove permanent harm, that defendant Mython won't be prejudiced or harmed by a prohibition on mining until trial several months from now, and that an injunction is in the public interest. But that can't happen at all unless the plaintiffs Mound People Coalition and People of the Dune have shown there is a substantial likelihood of succeeding on the legal basis of their claims. If they have not, there is no claim for the court to consider. So, it follows, then, that I will decide the defendant's motion first: if the law does not embrace the plaintiffs' claims, it necessarily follows that plaintiffs cannot show a likelihood of success and that the case must be dismissed. If there is no claim, then there is no need to consider the plaintiffs' request for an injunction, and the current temporary injunction would be dissolved.

First, turning to defendant Mython's motion to dismiss, the law requires me to assume the facts in the plaintiffs' complaint to be true. Because I've heard a lot of evidence regarding plaintiffs' claims and the dune, a mound, the impairment of what plaintiffs argue is protected as special or unique, or even sacred according to some witnesses, I will view that evidence in a light most favorable to plaintiffs' claims.

So, what about the law? Defendants argue that there are no constitutional provisions, no law passed by the legislature, and no common law legal precedents that support plaintiffs' claims. Legal precedents are the legal principles according to the decisions of appellate courts. If there is no law to support plaintiffs' claims, I do not have the judicial power to rule in favor of the plaintiffs at all.

*   *   *

An explanation is in order. Do you see this sculpture of Lady Justice on the bench next to me? She's in robes, blindfolded, holding a scale, and sword. She can be traced back to the Greek goddess Themis in 700 B.C. Themis stands for order, law, or custom. Other cultures have similar images of a woman who stands for justice. She interpreted what the gods wanted of humans. When the Romans adopted her from the Greeks, they changed her name to Justicia. She is associated with divine goodness, justice, purity, innocence, and wisdom to weigh evidence and values in exercising judgment. Lady Justice had no blindfold in ancient times. The blindfold appeared much later in protest of the harsh treatment of the poor by the early courts of law in England. Today, the blindfold symbolizes a belief or, to some, an illusion that justice is blind to bias or personal opinion: a judge must grant relief based on the law no matter what a judge personally feels or thinks from her or his experience.

*   *   *

The Mound People Coalition claims that the law limits the defendant's deed and right to mine because their cultural and sacred relationship precedes any title to defendant Mython from the United States down to today, that these values were not conveyed by this succession of deeds to defendant, and, therefore, its right to mine or extract is not part of its private property.

*   *   *

Witnesses for plaintiffs Mound People Coalition and Mr. Creek, who has lived at the foot of the dune for more than seventy years, claim they have inherited the land and that their cultural and spiritual relationship with the mound derived from a chain of ancient civilizations of mound builders that were not conveyed by our country's law of property and marketable titles to legally surveyed and described parcels of land dating back one hundred and fifty to two hundred years. These plaintiffs point to the testimony of archaeologists and anthropologists who have spent lifetimes studying mounds, their bones, fragments of wares, tools, and other artifacts, piecing together a picture of these ancient people. Mr. Creek testified that he'd heard from oral history about some legend he thinks that tells a story of the origin of mounds in this region where we live. Although of questionable reliability, he said he has sensed the presence of something under the dune, which he thinks is the mound. He says he picked up slight readings on his electromagnetic so-called ghost meter, but that they look different than what a ghost reading looks like. The tribes and Mr. Creek say the sacred mound buried beneath the dune, filled with the bones and ceremonial and cultural artifacts, gives them paramount "rights" that prohibit the defendant here from exercising its property rights to mine. The tribes testified that the rights of the mound itself precede and are embedded in the land and culture of their people and those who have occupied this land since the first mounds were built in this region between 2000 and 1000 BCE. Evidence of mound builders is more prevalent since 800 CE, well before the plaintiff Mound People Coalition tribes' Treaty of 1836 with the

United States. The tribes claim that the treaty did not convey their relationship to the land, the plants, and animals; that in any event this relationship and the tribes' uses long precede the government's patent offices, its surveyed town-range grid system of legal boundaries, or its history of a chain of title or deeds conveying title the last one hundred and fifty years favoring the defendant.

Does the law recognize and protect an ancient mound with artifacts and antiquities such that it would prohibit defendant from exercising its property right to mine? Did the cultural relationship to a thousand-year-old mound, if it exists, pass onto and remain with plaintiff-tribes? If so, did the Odawa (sometimes referred to as Ottawa) and Ojibwe (sometimes referred to as Chippewa) treaty with the United States relinquish this relationship where no mention is made of it in the treaty?

*   *   *

I understand the frustration the plaintiffs and many of you in this courtroom must feel by the threatened loss of the dune or mound. But there is no law, no constitutional declaration, nothing presented in this case that recognizes that an ancient Indian mound, if it exists, is protected from mining. There are laws that protect tribal artifacts and antiquities, but these do not prevent a landowner from flattening the dune or mound. In fact, these laws provide only that artifacts must be identified and turned over to the tribe.

Regrettably, as described by the archeologists' testimony, thousands of mounds have been destroyed throughout the country because of the rights of property, our expanding population, economy, and consumption of resources. But until the law protects them, there is no claim. The tribal plaintiffs claim their treaties never conveyed their cultural relationship to a mound, but the treaty cases only recognize their rights to fish, gather, and hunt. Further, even assuming the mound exists under the Voyager Dune, there's no legal proof tying the present Odawa and Ojibwe tribes, represented by the plaintiff Mound People Coalition, to the mound. And Mr. Creek's testimony is based on his subjective senses and readings he noticed on what is basically a ghost meter.

But even before I can answer these questions, has it been shown that there is a mound at all? I understand the frustration the plaintiffs and many of you in this courtroom must feel by the threatened loss of the dune or possible mound. The law puts the burden of proof on plaintiffs, including the tribes and Mr. Creek. They have not shown by objective evidence that this mound exists under the dune. And, even if a mound exists, there is no legal theory that establishes a paramount cultural interest that limits the defendant's property right to mine. I have no choice, despite what I may think personally. Accordingly, the defendant's motion for summary judgment is granted, and the Mound People Coalition's and Mr. Creek's claims are dismissed.

* * *

Second, taking up the claim of plaintiff, People of the Dune, and its entourage of supporting organizations who are intervening parties in this case, the analysis is similar. They theorize that because these millennial dunes are dynamic, always shifting and moving, and of a special character, there is a common property interest in the continuation of the three hundred miles of coastal dunes free from defendant's alteration or disruption of the dune. They submitted testimony through geologists, soil scientists, and biologists showing the unique and rare formation, vegetation, and ecosystem of the Voyager and all coastal dunes along this inland sea. They argued that a rare, unique property of a special character essential to all people establishes an interest in the community that limits the defendant's private right to extract and remove the dune from the coastline. For purposes of my decision, I find that without question the Voyager Dune is part of a rare, continuous, and moving coastal dune system, and that they are of a special character and important to the public and larger community; the Voyager Dune and coastal dune system are unique to the world.

The primary question is a legal one: Is there any law, constitution, or common law court decision that limits the property right to mine to protect the Voyager Dune in this case?

First, there are no constitutional or legislatively enacted laws of which I am aware that create a public common property interest that is paramount to the right of private property to mine the dune. Second, the argument that under common law the owner of rare, unique property of a special character is limited or prevented from mining its property is intriguing. It is true that the government could pass laws to limit mining further under the exercise of its regulatory power. But as noted, it hasn't. Therefore, I conclude that there is no common law rule of property that limits the rights of the defendant to extract the fruits and profits that spring from its private ownership of the dune.

If anything, our federal and state constitutions protect private property and the rights that go with it from being taken for private use, or if taken for a proper public use, then not without just compensation or money to make them whole. As the chief of the state's geological survey testified yesterday, "Our agency must honor private property rights of landowners to mine and extract sand, gravel, minerals, ore, oil, natural gas, and sand from their land." I'm not sure I agree with his statement. When it comes to the value of public rights or values, I question just compensation or money as a measure of what may well transcend economic values. As the lawyers on both sides in this case have pointed out, there are well-established public rights in waters that are public and place a duty on government to protect these waters and public rights under what is known as common law public trust doctrine. But while subject to an intriguing, palpable argument, it is a doctrine limited to navigable waters. And this does not alter the letter of the law that private ownership of land carries with it a "bundle of sticks" and that those sticks grant exclusive possession within the legal surveyed boundaries of defendant's property; this "bundle of sticks" grants the owner of land the right to extract the maximum "fruits" of economic value. Parenthetically, I realize that the word "fruits" may be a poor metaphor for some of you, but like it or not, the common law of private property is not limited by the existence of interests others might claim are unique or sacred to a community. As suggested by the blindfold on Lady Justice, referring to the statuette right here on my bench next to me, justice and the law are not necessarily one and the same.

During oral arguments, witnesses from the International Union of the Conservation of Nature testified that the Voyager Dune has its own right to exist as an indigenous cultural relationship, beyond private property, with a paramount right of protection. Lawyers for the plaintiffs also argue that since these dunes have continued since the last Ice Age, and continue to shift and move, these special coastal dunes should be recognized as commons, like the water of which the dunes are a part, suggesting the dunes are like a living being with rights somehow inherent in defendant Mython's property. But, again, there is no law that recognizes a dune is a commons or person with legal rights. And even if a law did so, it would not as a practical matter alter anything that the law can't or does not already address. For example, if there is a right in the dune itself, the organizations would still have to file a claim that establishes a violation of the right. While dunes move, as the experts said, it would take a geological age for them to get to the courthouse. For further explanation, I will add a postscript on this point when my office transcribes this bench opinion and releases it to the attorneys, their clients, and the public.

I don't doubt the existence of these high public values and perceptions. Most people in one way or another sense the graces of nature. But how does a court of law deal with these immeasurable values? Isn't that why people come together and amend state or federal constitutions, like equal protection, women's right of property, and suffrage? This may sound like apologetics on my part, but it is not. As I explained at the beginning, I can have one view that is beyond law; it may even perceive the truth or beauty of a higher justice. But without a legal or constitutional principle that recognizes this, I cannot entertain the plaintiffs' claims.

In conclusion, then, plaintiffs and their intervening parties have no legal claim recognized by the law. The defendant Mython's motion is granted, and the plaintiffs' case is dismissed.

Gasps rippled through the air. Pandemonium. Loud cries and stomping of feet shook the bookcases, rattled the brass light fixtures and opaque beveled glass-paneled doors at the entrance to the courtroom. Dust floated over the crowd in the late afternoon light as Judge Odie Holmes strode into his chambers. People in the hall pushed back into the courtroom, pressed in on the corporation's attorneys, and surrounded the citizen and tribal attorneys' tables; the bailiff and another officer on hand brought order, not without vocal condemnations. TV news cameras were whirring. Cell phone cameras were clicking. Judge Holmes came back to the bench, greeted by a wall of grumbling and growling, his robe already open, exposing his T-shirt and snap-on collar and tie.

(Back on the record, 9:43 p.m.)

Judge Holmes: Please, there's one other matter. I am ordering that this decision and order shall not take effect for seventy-two hours from the time of entry (the judge looked at his watch), which means three days from ten o'clock in the morning, tomorrow. The defendant, for the sake of keeping the peace, shall not take any action to enter the property and begin mining until the expiration of the three days. Those people at the encampment who are members of any of the parties before me shall remove everything and themselves from the property by the end of the three days. I intend cooperation from all of you.

IT IS SO ORDERED.

POSTSCRIPT TO BENCH OPINION

A right in nature or the dune is intriguing, but itself does not really advance protection of the dune. It seems that it could grant some persons or organizations the right to file a suit in the name of a natural feature or object—a river, lake, mountain, forest, or a dune—like a trustee on behalf of heirs or a guardian for a child or other legally incapacitated person. But in most instances citizens already have standing in varying degrees to file these kinds of lawsuits, the case before me but one. See Christopher Stone, *Should Trees Have Standing?* (Oxford University Press, 3rd Ed., 2010) (legal rights for natural objects). Today, if a person or members of an organization can demonstrate an actual or threatened harm to a use or interest protected by law, and a court can do something about it, the person or organization has standing.

Even if a right in nature or beingness of a river, lake, or other feature is recognized, who files the case? Anyone? Wouldn't it require someone who has a relationship with the natural object or being to represent it? How would anyone without a connection to a natural object, such as a rare dune, show sufficient interest to bring a lawsuit? Would someone with an alleged interest like Mr. Creek, the Mound People Coalition, a tribal member, or People of the Dune be the right person or group?

But this becomes circular. If a natural object is a "being," then it is not a human who is the plaintiff or "person" bringing the lawsuit; it is the natural object, not the human being, which claims the threatened harm. But for the natural object to bring a lawsuit, it obviously takes an action by a human who brings the suit on behalf of the natural being or object (e.g., as noted above, as a trustee or guardian). … (After all, trees or dunes cannot march into the courthouse from the ridge west of the city. Although a tree entered the courthouse last April when half the crown of the silver maple in the side yard crashed through the row of windows in this very courtroom. Water from the river behind the courthouse hasn't gushed into the clerk's office to file a suit. Not yet anyway. The weather is shattering records year after year—who can say this will not happen in the future.)

What I'm saying is this: for the dune or tree to prove that the defendant's activity will impair the dune, it takes a person to file the suit. Someone would have to file a lawsuit asserting the right on behalf of a natural being, show that the law recognizes a legal claim to protect the natural being from harm, prove the harm exists or will occur, and, finally, demonstrate a court order that will address the harm. In substance, this is not much different than what humans or nonprofit organizations have done throughout the country these past seventy years. The only way I can conceive rights in nature will be effective is in their educational and transformative value about how we view and live in relation to nature and our environment. Once this changes the culture, laws or constitutional amendments (like women's suffrage and civil rights constitutional amendments and laws) could be enacted. This would have influence because these new amendments and laws would recognize that nature itself is the "person" or entity harmed, triggering the rights of those with an interest in protecting the natural entity or being to vest courts with jurisdiction to entertain the suit. Unfortunately, that does not help the plaintiffs' cause or claims in the lawsuit before me, because to my knowledge no such constitutional provision or law exists or has been presented.

I would add, that based on the bigger picture of the immediate harm that humanity and the world face at this time in history (human population soaring over 8 billion people, loss of quality of life, pollution, and the grim prospects from war and climate change), the time it would take for this cultural transformation and enactment of new laws or amendments to constitutions in my opinion will take too long to make a difference anyway. Are we doomed by our own notions of justice and jurisprudence? Who knows? There's always the sudden cultural change out of sheer necessity, like the mass migrations that followed the advance and retreat of glaciers in the ice ages, or the "One Hundred Monkeys" parable. The sooner the better.

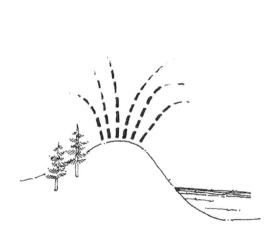

NIGHTMARE

In the middle
of the night
on the day Mython
would start mining,
Judge Odom yelled
something in
his sleep …

All that night, like vultures circling their prey, Mython's minions mobilized for a feeding frenzy. Trucks towed construction trailers, and machinery rumbled into the entrance road that pointed to the shadowed belly of the dune. Soon after, a caravan of more trucks, dump trucks, cars, and workers invaded the staging area, followed by a double-wide flatbed, an eighteen-wheeler semi with the massive shovel, diesel engines, twin generators, and two more trucks carrying loads of steel beams, tanks, parts, and equipment. The stage was set for the final act: portable pole barns, tanks for fuel, machine shop, waste pits and pump and haul stations, and parking areas. They moved in front-end loaders, dozers, graders, and other equipment, converted shipping-container toilets, then the beams, and the gauged track conveyor system to transport the sand from the giant shovel ready to bite the center of the dune. The calamitous noise filled the night, the pounding of wheels and of heavy equipment shook the ground, causing the tents to wobble. Sleepless campers jumped up, and put on hiking boots and shoes, dark pants and shirts, and headlamps. They formed lines with 150 people each, seven deep, along the edge of the picnic area at the base of the dune. Solon Creek sat facing the dune in a campfire vigil in his weathered Adirondack chair.

Judge Holmes kicked at the bed sheets and snapped up, into a sitting position. His wife, Harriet, reached for him as he slid out of bed. "Odie, what is it?"

"I can't sleep," he said. "I'm going to my office."

He couldn't remember what he had yelled as he awoke, but he had dreamed something, felt a shiver through his limbs. The nightmare came back to him. *He stumbled through a dark forest toward an opening with milky white light. He could see it was a meadow covered in a luminous fog. When he stepped into the clearing, the fog enveloped him. He saw the dim figure of a man. A voice called to him: "Stop. Come. Come with me. You must see the mound." The fog thickened, blanketed him, and it seemed as if the fog was lifting him off the ground. He kicked to escape, but the meadow fell away. He rose into the sky, went limp ... drifted over a vast sea ... saw what looked like a ridge along the shore. As he drifted farther, the ridge was sand, a dune, a whirlwind blew the sand off the ridge ... there below him he saw the shape of an animal ... cougar ... or panther. Then the blanket of fog dissipated, nothing, a void, and he felt as if he was falling, falling through time until ... He was standing in the meadow. A woman draped in flowing robes floated toward him ... in one hand she held scales with something red ... beating, a beating heart tottering on the scales ... in the other, she held a sword. A blindfold hung down from her eyes ... sorrowful eyes ... weeping eyes. He heard her saying something ... Yes, that was it. "Take off my blindfold. Clean the rust from my sword. Protect my heart ..."*

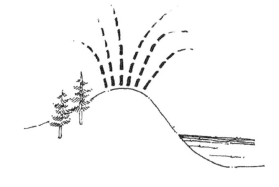

A METANOIA

My Karma ran over
my dogma ...[1]

Judge Holmes stood near the driver's side of his car, keys in hand, and searched for answers in the vast galaxy of the Milky Way stretched across the sky. A mound, the tribes, the dune itself. Lady Justice. Had he betrayed Lady Justice, betrayed what drove him to become a judge? A memory of his first day in law school popped into his head. He had walked through double mahogany doors and looked up a worn marble stairway. The voice of an older student at the top of the steps echoed in the entryway. "Remember. When you walk out of here three years from now, the circuits in your brain will never be the same." He'd felt a flutter in his abdomen but paid no attention. Now he wondered if this had been true. By thirty, he'd felt old, analyzing everyone and everything he saw as object, cause and effect, the pieces of a puzzle to be hammered or squeezed into the squares and holes of legalese.

The headlights cast a glow under a canopy of trees as he turned onto the main highway to the city. He parked and climbed out of the jeep as the bell in the courthouse clock-tower clanged once. He punched the password into the bolt-lock keypad, climbed the stairs to his chambers, and switched on the lights. Files, books, and papers he'd used for his bench opinion lay scattered on his desk. He looked, as he always did, at the long, narrow Chinese print on the wall that he'd purchased during a trip to China with his wife: a figure of a bearded man on a ledge beneath a gnarled wispy pine tree gazed into the solitude of a deep valley and snow-covered mountains. Below the figure, a lake was shrouded in mist. Judge Holmes sighed. He felt a longing when he'd read Han Shan or saw the calligraphy and poetry of the ancients at a place called Shisen-do near Kyoto during a judges' exchange program.

The clock on his desk ticked six minutes after one. He turned on the PC and clicked for a new document … He picked up the hammered-bronze statue of Lady Justice from the corner of the desk, and his hands began to shake. The nightmare came back to him. A bolt of adrenaline shocked him. Words shot through his fingers as if they were no longer his own. He had nine hours.

The red-eyed early morning headlines seemed ominous.

COURT DECIDES FATE OF VOYAGER DUNE

PROTESTERS FORM HUMAN WALL
TO GUARD DUNE

TRIBAL DRUMS SUMMON ANCESTORS
TO DEFEND SPIRIT MOUND

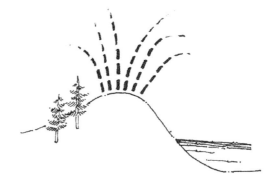

EXCERPTS FROM THE DISSENTING OPINION OF JUDGE ODOM HOLMES

There are benefits
of a river that might
escape a lawyer's view ...[2]

---

2 Hudson County Water Co. v McCarter, 209 U.S. 349, 357 (1908), where
   Justice Oliver Wendell Holmes (no relation) embraced experience as the raison
   d'etre of justice and the law.

JUDGE ODOM R. HOLMES, CIRCUIT JUDGE

I dissent from my own opinion and order, entered three days ago. The order dissolved the temporary order against mining the dune and dismissed the plaintiffs' claim for a permanent injunction to stop the project.

> [EXPLANATORY NOTE: Admittedly, this is unorthodox, but there is nothing in the court rules that prohibit a judge from doing so. There is something else that is unorthodox. While I will honor my judicial duty to write this as a formal opinion (facts, law, law applied to facts, conclusion, and footnotes to citations), as I write this opinion, I will interject a more personal subtext, indented and in different typeface, to record, distinct from footnotes, my inner thoughts and process as I write this opinion and arrive at my conclusion.]

> *For starters, I'm not yet sure what happened to my juridical beliefs since my opinion and order, a belief that relied, has relied for years, on the soundness of firm rules of law, tight legal logic, trusting no matter what, that loyal adherence to their application fulfilled my role as a judge. It is not for me to harmonize my experience with the rule of law. But now I realize that I no longer can sit by and watch an intolerable ubiquitous demise of a world in which I live … sitting here as circuit judge, I'm compelled to test this belief, but in doing so not abandon my duty as judge.*

In the Order, I decided that (1) under traditional rules of burden of proof, the plaintiff tribes did not show by the weight of evidence that there is a mound, and (2) assuming the existence of a mound and accepting the finding that the Voyager Dune is rare, unique, and of a special character, there is nothing in the common law that operates as a limitation on the defendant's private property right to mine and remove the Voyager Dune. I will now revisit both of these rulings.

This dissent is framed by both the reality of the dune and the role and extent of the law of private property and the rights that go with it, sometimes referred to as a "buddle of sticks": the right of exclusive possession, right to use, do, or right to extract anything in, on, or over the property. But in the third decade of the 21st century, perhaps before, there is a growing realization that there is a disconnect between the unbridled expectations of those who own and extract the things from the land and the magnitude of damages and costs to the commons that underlay the viability of the natural world and people—a clash with the extremities of the extractive economy—what Supreme Court Justice William Douglas dubbed the "great God Progress." Justice Douglas (in his own dissent to an order that let a mining company discharge asbestos-fibered tailings into the waters of Lake Superior) observed that there are outside limits on private property when it comes to punishing nature's commons and humanity.[3]

> *We homo sapiens have a split, dual personality, no surprise, part of so many intersecting dualities of life that are becoming far too evident in the increasing intensity of division and layers of conflicts in the world. Granted, this is nothing new, the world, human lives, our lives seem to be full of competing relative realities, in conflict or ambiguity about choices, meaning, and existence itself. Watching the day-to-day conflicts in my little microcosm of the world that have come before me as a judge for more than two decades, they seem mostly about one individual or group against another*

---

3 Minnesota v Reserve Mining Co., 419 U.S. 802, 95 S. Ct. 287(1974) (Justice Douglas, dissenting). Supreme Court Justice William O. Douglas (1898–1980) dissented to the lifting of an injunction to allow a mining company's discharge of minute cancer-causing asbestos tailings into Lake Superior.

over their own perceptions, wants, and desires. But in the midst of these narrow adversarial disputes, other values and contexts sometimes emerge beyond what the parties or I can see. And, then there is sorting out reality itself, the existence and interaction of human nature and the physical world, the experience of life at all levels, including dimensions unknown to us. I can see a one-hundred twenty-foot tall white pine or ancient sugar maple in my front yard as an obstacle to sunlight reaching the patio and cut it down. My neighbor may see it as a home for sap and songbirds. It doesn't change the fact that no matter what I think or feel, these trees are still trees in what I might think of as their "beingness."

Justice Douglas wrote: "If … there is doubt, it should be resolved in favor of humanity, lest in the end our judicial system be part and parcel of a regime that makes people, the sovereign power in this Nation, the victims of the great God Progress which is behind the stay permitting this vast pollution of Lake Superior and its environs. I am not aware of a constitutional principle that allows either private or public enterprises to despoil any part of the domain that belongs to all of the people. Our guiding principle should be Mr. Justice Holmes' dictum that our waterways, great and small, are treasures, not garbage dumps or cesspools."[4]

The "great God Progress" may well have become the "great devil progress," given that it may well have exceeded its useful rationalization in face of the realization that the necessities for survival are festering in existential peril. (I just had this thought: Maybe someone ought to file a petition to place the earth into federal bankruptcy or receivership (28 U.S. 3103); the appointed trustee could collect from those who are indebted and have caused damage to our air, water, ecosystems, public infrastructure, and other property and public rights: a bankruptcy judge could force those demanding to be

....

4   Id.

paid, the creditors, to take less, consume less—a bankruptcy compels those with claims or who owe the bankrupt estate to lower their expectations, so that whatever is left of the bankrupt estate is preserved to give it a chance to survive. I realize a bankruptcy court is not a perfect analogy, in the sense that the estate is often viewed as a list of assets, first to add assets to the estate from those who have an obligation to the estate, and second to see that those whose claims on the estate lower their expectations of collecting—in this instance the demands on nature and natural systems on which all life depends. But is the natural world merely an asset measured by dollars or other currency? Nature is the person asking the court to free it from the punishing demands and effects on the commons, earth, people, and life caused by others. Perhaps, the better analogy is a receivership, where a trustee would reorganize and free earth from the demands on earth and its people from the grip of impacts caused by the exercise and demands of others on the natural systems that support them … The point is, bankruptcy would order those responsible to restore and foot the bill for the damage, pay for that which is forever lost, and restore the balance and keep the planet from wobbling off course … a redemption of sorts, although a redemption beyond the law will happen anyway, if earth veers off course more than it is. The point is, if bankruptcy requires a reduction of expectations as a right of property, it would also reduce the claims and demands caused by the extractors and consumers that have far exceeded the capacity of earth to fulfill them. So why wait for bankruptcy, why not lower expectations to conform to reality? Sooner or later, we'll have to conform, so, as I said before, the sooner the better …

*   *   *

With the pressing collapse of earth's viability (e.g., the water cycle, biological diversity, climate, and so much more), it may be that the punishing expectations and entitlement of the law of private property can no longer be tolerated. The earth's viability for supporting life is in the crosshairs. How did the right of private property get to the point where it leads to the death of nature's web on which all life, even the right to property and profits, depends? Are private property and property rights really a "sacred cow," immune from judicial interference or limitation? Is private property so exclusive that it doesn't matter what happens to the patterns that connect nature's commons?

> *If this sounds like apologetics, it is not. Nature's not a doctrine! If this seems like a justification for the legal abolishment of private property rights, it is not. But we are not isolated atomistic objects, mechanistically bouncing off each other by cause and effect like Newton's cradle experiment (balls hung on strings from a bar, lift one and drop it, it strikes the ball next to it and so on … until the ball on the opposite end pops up equal distance to the ball that is dropped … the proverbial "for every action there is an equal and opposite reaction"). I struggled with this in my bench opinion three days ago when I tried to explain Lady Justice's blindfold and scales. As I write this now, Lady Justice's eyes look back at me … blindfold pulled down to her shoulders, heart on her scales. What wasn't I seeing before? Are my own experiences (or human experience) of nature, aesthetics, art … a lifetime of looking at a ridgeline on the other side of a bay as much a part in the weighing of justice as is reason or the right to exploit property? I recall reading the book by the eighteenth-century Jesuit Jean Pierre de Caussade who, drawing on St. Teresa's Interior Castle: "God makes known much more by the heart than the mind, which ponders and reasons." Hildegard of Bingen, and numerous mystics, philosophers, and the cultures of Indigenous people have long carried the same awareness or wisdom.*

Supreme Court jurist Justice Holmes also observed, "The life of the law has not been logic; it is experience."[5]

----

5 Oliver Wendell Holmes, *The Common Law*, Little, Brown and Company (1923).

Talk about experience. We can last only a few days without water—fatigue, nausea, organ failure, and death follows. As Jacques Cousteau once said, "The water cycle and life cycle are one." But morbidity aside, experiencing nature for most of us, no matter our walk of life, we glimpse something in the water, the sky, and nature, the angle of light on a path in the woods or a ridgeline that we cannot describe, but sense as a whole.

Is this why Justice Holmes wrote another opinion that blocked the diversion of New Jersey's Passaic River: "There are benefits of a river that might escape a lawyer's view."[6]

Perhaps, this dissent from myself opens a window where the graces of nature and art may not escape the view of the law. Years ago, I took a poetry class, a few years after I was elected circuit court judge ... I had started feeling far too old and rigid for my age ... still remember the startling effect when I read a line from W.B. Yeats, "God guard me from those thoughts men think in the mind alone." (The Collected Poems of W.B. Yeats) Oddly, the realization hit me again in a divorce case when a husband and wife reached a property settlement except for the last two items of property—an MP3 player and coffee maker; neither one could let go ... the wife offered the MP3 player, he refused; the husband offered the coffee maker, she refused; the wife offered him the coffee maker, he refused ... It went back and forth like this for an hour. I adjourned the session, chiding them that if they couldn't divide the last two items of their marital estate, maybe they should think about reconciling, after which I escaped to a small pub hidden in the back room of a nearby hotel, ordered a double, sipped whiskey, slight burn to my throat, then noticed my fingers tapping a rhythm on the tabletop: accent, unaccent, accent, unaccent ... switching from stressed to unstressed, unstressed to stressed ... but what

6 Hudson County Water Co. v McCarter, 208 U.S. at 357 (1908).

did I know … Next thing I knew I jotted down, something about … Lady Justice … have we turned our back the / edge of your sword, a rusted / blade of words slashes the air / we the ones who are blind … (jumbled four and three meters per line … these stanzas nothing more than a therapeutic lament buried in a graveyard of file boxes) … The couple reconciled, their hearts clinging to the last two items of their marital property … Now, here I am wondering about Lady Justice again. Is there something present in conflict beyond the material transactions between people, earth, and property?

How, I ask, can justice not be the same, albeit with a different face, as truth and beauty? Should the law therefore not conform to or embrace this greater reality at a time of existential crisis between humanity and the earth? Nature, the earth, and its species preexisted us in flesh—spirit being a different but perhaps not inseparable reality and mystery beyond our comprehension—sustained itself quite well with all the wide-ranging, sudden, and eon-long upheavals and changes millions of years before sapiens showed up on the scene.

When it comes to us sapiens—meaning wise and sagacious, a rather presumptuous anthropocentric mindset—is it the responsibility of a judge, as Yeats observed, to guard us sapiens from destroying the earth, that is, by those thoughts we "think in the mind alone?" Will Descartes ("I think therefore I am") … the industrial revolution foretold … have the last word? What about the centuries-long, drawn-out battle between Marx and Locke: should the owner class or the workers control the resources and means of production? How did these two poles end up in the hands of a few wealthy individuals who own corporations or in Russia, for example, a politburo? What's the difference, they're both about hierarchical control over parts of the same economic equation. Why do we allow reality to even be defined by these two controlling poles? I ask, again: are we nothing but Newtonian pith-balls under the control of the experimenters, for every

action there is a reaction no matter what the cost? Is a for-
ested hillside nothing more than a resource for the sawmill or
real estate development for profit with a view? Is a pristine,
cold-water lake nothing but a reservoir for someone to own,
tap, and sell as a commodity? Can someone own or destroy
the water cycle? Is one of the premises of our existential crisis
based on a myth or idea that defines existence as "resources"
or "products," and not as a river or lake? A ravenous entitle-
ment to extract nature has come at such great cost to people,
community, and our planet. As already suggested, this seems
to be a denial of reality. Perhaps, it started with the bite of
an apple from the tree of knowledge ... except now it seems
we sapiens are going after the tree of life itself.

*   *   *

The question that haunts me is this: Can or did the law ever con-
done an undisputed loss and demise of the earth's commons: forests,
mountain tops, lakes, rivers, marshes, or as in this case a gap in the
unbroken chain of twelve-thousand-year-old dunes?

What about the commons, the aesthetic and psychologi-
cal or healthy values that make up a town or city? I have
observed a few things over the years within the counties
over which this court has jurisdiction: the cutting down of
large willows shading a river to make room for steel walls
to hold a riverbank for private condominiums; the loss of
shores and beaches where grandparents and grandchildren
swam, picnicked, or fished; the loss of wetlands and flood-
plains connected to creeks—civilization's flood control and
treatment of runoff from rains—ocean river mouths, lakes
now "dead zones" from our glutenous farming practices
and human and animal feed wastes; flattening of glacial
ridgelines intertwined with a city's psyche and aesthete;
modern edifices blocking vistas of a bay; lick-a-brick sided
pole buildings that eat away at the values that people share
as a whole, a visual violence that seethes and undermines

the lives of people, neighborhoods, the community … This brings to mind Wendell Berry's Another Turn of the Crank *and his essay about "forest and community" and "private property and commonwealth." Is income and cost limited to the viewpoint of the individual property owner? What about the forest? I once issued an order that halted a suburban transplant from shooting a street-sized driveway straight down a forested hillside through a cold-water seep to reach the garage to an enormous neo-colonial house on the lakeshore. The forty-eight-degree seep fostered one of a few patches in North America of a rare yellow, tiny daisy-like monkey flower (Erythranthe guttata syn mimulus guttatus). I did so because the threatened loss of the monkey flower and its rare micro-ecosystem transcended the self-interest of the landowner. It didn't seem to me the desire of the owner could dictate the location, design, or scale of the driveway. Is the rare coastal dune system that will be severed by the mining in this case similar to the monkey flower? Is there a principle in common law that allows a judge, given the right circumstances, to step in, limit the right of a property owner, and protect a preexisting distinctive feature of nature like the Voyager Dune or its coastal dune system, the shared common value of a community?*

*   *   *

In my Bench Opinion a few days ago, I ruled that the Mound People Coalition failed to carry its burden of proof that a mound exists. Traditionally, the burden of proof is on the person or entity bringing the lawsuit—the plaintiff. This is because a lawsuit seeks a final judgment that would change the status quo of the existing relationship, rights, and responsibilities between the plaintiff and the person sued—the defendant. But what about protecting the status quo of humanity's rights, responsibilities, and relationship to a special commons of rare or necessary features of biological, physical, historical, or cultural importance? Traditionally, a plaintiff like the Mound People Coalition must prove that a defendant's exercise of its right to mine will be harmful to the plaintiffs in some way and in violation of some law. Typically, like Mython Corporation, mining companies argue that the mineral deposits are where they find them when they purchase the land. But isn't it equally true that rare or special features like the mound (if it exists) or a commons of rare or special value to society are also only where you find them? The tribes here claim that the right to mine itself will alter a culturally and spiritually sacred mound that so far has not been proven to exist under the dune. Their claim—based on their relationship to the mound and dune—may have as much or more value than the defendant's claimed property right. The mound is alleged to exist, but the evidence, although admittedly conjecture, would tie its value to an ancient civilization. So, this is not just about the defendant's right to mine the property and the tribe's right to sue to stop the mine, but about a natural feature of cultural or even sacred value, a claimed fundamental relationship that would preexist both the plaintiff tribes and organizations, and the defendant Mython's purchase of Voyager Dune.

Fifty years ago, there was a case involving a dock and dredging company that started excavating the lands under the Detroit River for a marina on Grosse Isle, an island downriver from the city. The state and others filed a lawsuit to stop it because the waters and lands of the Detroit River, like any navigable waters and the lands under them, are owned by the public and held by government as trustee for the benefit of its citizen beneficiaries (the legal principle is called the public trust doctrine, which I will address later in this dissent). The dredging company answered that the burden of proof was on the state and people to show that the waters and lands in question were of substantial and special public value: if this could not be shown, there was no claim. But the appellate court disagreed and said, "No."[7] When the common lands and waters of a state are involved, the public value is presumed, so the burden of proof was on the dredging company to prove that there was no special public value. In another case, a court granted an injunction requiring the defendant corporation to start cleaning up groundwater pollution before a final decision deemed that it was responsible, because the Court recognized that ongoing

....
7 Township of Grosse Isle v Dredging Company, 15 Mich App 556 (1969).

pollution from a release of toxic substances existed on the site and that the real relationship was not the defendant's property rights, but "the status quo ante is an unpolluted environment."[8] Is there a pattern in nature so essential that there is something common and inherent in the land, the air, the water itself, no matter who owns it? This is enough to warrant rethinking who has burden of proof in a case like the mining of the Voyager Dune.

> *So, this was a case where a panel of judges recognized the special character and value of land (underwater) in its natural state. It was up to the defendant or person wanting to alter this special character, the status quo, to prove it had little or no public value, or that if it had such special public value, then to show that its dredging would not impair the value. In a sense, it qualifies or limits the right of use, because shifting the burden of proof embraces the ontological essence or beingness of the water and land under it. But we sapiens don't like to put limits on ourselves, certainly not because of the existence or beingness of a tree, river, lake, or a coastal dune that would interfere with wealth, power, and control. Given the state of the world, do we ever put any limits on ourselves? Isn't that the curse? At most it seems to me that our idea of recognizing a higher value is to study the problem and postpone any limitation on ourselves until it's too late to do anything about it.*

To return to what haunts me: can law embrace the pattern that connects nature and us human sapiens as a whole? What is it in the law of property that is missing? Property, rights of use, and extraction … but what of the responsibility in the law of each of us to others—people, or a river, lake, or three-hundred-year-old tree? And what about the cultural relationship of ourselves and others to a river, lake, tree, or other species? What rights and responsibilities must be accounted for if our relationship to nature is of necessity common and fundamental to our existence? This points toward a

---

8   Attorney General v Thomas Solvent, 146 Mich App 55 (1985).

respect for nature in its natural state or cultural relationship that may exist between people and nature, despite the traditional right of the defendant to insist that a plaintiff, the injured property owner, or natural feature represented by those who have a cultural relationship, have no claim.

> *I've often wondered about nuisance cases before me, where a neighbor injured by noise, noxious fumes, or discharge of harmful substances must prove interference with his or her use and enjoyment of property when it comes to the air and water or natural resources. Why do courts have to wait for interference or injury to the neighbor before they can step in to address the fumes, noise, or danger? No wonder pollution despite the presence of environmental laws has incrementally caused ubiquitous effects and harm to the earth that are now systemic. We resolve local disputes after it's too late, often without regard to the impact on the whole ... I had a case a few years ago in a county east of here where the state highway department wanted to cut down a mile-long crown of old maple trees planted by the Conservation Corps during last century's depression that were located by a highway. They wanted to remove the trees to save the expense from having to maintain them and the life of a reckless driver who drove thirty feet off the road. The trees couldn't march to the courthouse, so, a group of residents and farmers brought a lawsuit to save the trees, because for over 75 years these trees had taken on special meaning and value to them. I asked the lawyers if the trees had become more valuable to those in the community than just a highway. Heeding where my question might be going, the state's attorney voluntarily withdrew the plan except for a few dead trees. It saved me having to rule on the matter ... Based on the law I'm not sure I could have ruled in favor of the trees ... sometimes broad legal principles that embrace transcendent values bring about a resolution without or with little judicial intervention.*

These cases are merely examples where the burden of proof

shifted to the defendants because the status quo did not only include the plaintiffs' and defendants' respective interests in property, but the preservation of the status quo of existing undisturbed public waters, land, or environment. Is there a common public value—call it an essential relationship—not just between the parties here, but between the dune to the whole of this ancient, dynamic coastal system and the public community that has come to understand and experience its special value? If the answer is "yes," how can this be incorporated in a decision that would respect a mound or rare dune with a shifting of traditional principles governing who has the burden of proof?

An artist friend dropped by my courtroom once to hear arguments about a proposed four-lane highway bridge over a dedicated natural river. On a walk after the hearing, he told me he'd listened to the lawyers' arguments on scientific impacts, costs, and benefits, lamenting no one said anything about the natural river, the setting, the artistic or higher values that seemed so present. I remember a law professor once said before a large assembly of judges (including the undersigned of this dissent), lawyers, and economists engaged to consider the law and risk to the environment, "Lately, I've been looking for answers around the halls of the theology school." A renowned economist shouted from the audience, "It's your job as a lawyer to fit the law into our carefully measured equations of costs and benefits based on our principles of economics that balance the various private and public interests in society." Isn't this a problem? Has the world slipped into a belief that economics … today we commonly translate as free markets or neoliberalism … or the "great God Progress" drives the law at the expense of justice … Lady Justice … ignores the experience of beauty, art, higher values, often present but immeasurable? Of course, I've read today economists want to put dollar signs on rainforests, rivers, North America's Great Lakes based on what are called ecosystem services or natural capital assets. Hedge funds even want to buy up and control the ecosystem's services based on their natural capital asset value, as if they owned the inherent natural processes of the earth … What? The oxygen-carbon exchange and cycle of the planet an asset or service for us humans? So, people can own and control and profit off of a contrived market that is premised on owning the natural feature as an asset? If Lake Superior has a natural capital asset value of seven hundred billion dollars, there will be trillionaires who may gladly capitalize it. If the natural processes of an ecosystem already exist, and the public value exists, then can it be impaired or destroyed by unregulated exercise of private property rights or markets in the first place? How can justice be achieved if the law is viewed more narrowly than the experience and reality of natural features and systems that already benefit the whole of the planet and society? And why is it that eco-systems are viewed in terms of the economic value of the services? Is a rainforest nothing more than an asset or resource to fit the equations of economic theory? Is a rainforest, the aboriginal forest far north of here in Canada, or a Great Lake like the inland sea that is part of the Voyager Dune's existence just an asset on someone's balance sheet or a hedge fund's commodity? This is wholly human-centered, and if so, it is purely utilitarian like the dredging that company wanted to build a marina. Were those tears in Lady Justice's eyes, without her blindfold? Her expression is of deep sorrow when the immeasurable beauty of the natural order of things and graces of nature are excluded from the experience of law and justice. Isn't this where law and justice become one and the same?

* * *

Are traditional legal principles like burden of proof and private property contrary to the natural order of things? It seems that when they are carried too far, they are opposed to, and do not conform to, the larger human experience of the natural world, part of reality. It is my view, that principles of law like real property should conform to the reality of beingness, the "isness" of nature and its natural order, and not just property rights that are superimposed on the natural world by legal boundaries and definitions. Shouldn't there be an imperative from the natural order of things—the patterns of nature as a whole—that the "ontological" essence or beingness of nature must be respected.

> *The word ontology comes from the Greek word "onto,"
> which is the study and experience of being and the natural
> order of things. While I could speculate, as the law profes-
> sor did, about the mystery of all of this in divine terms, for
> purposes of this opinion I use the word ontology ... which
> by definition prevents me from shutting off the experience,
> values, and graces arising out of the beingness of the natural
> world. I chose "ontology" here because I don't have to get
> into the nuances of ethics, morality, or theology ... I neither
> have the time, nor inclination to go there. And if I did, I'd
> think about poet Mary Oliver's perception about the ordi-
> nariness and graces in her experience of the natural world.
> The gorilla Ishmael in Daniel Quinn's book by the same
> name and his student ventured into theology, concluding
> that the story of human religions did nothing more than
> justify humanity's myths that it would conquer, control, and
> build a paradise on earth—a story that had so far led to
> utter destruction of the sort I've alluded to in the opinion or
> these personal musings. On the other hand, I'm not so sure
> this is entirely accurate, because as noted the Greek meaning
> of the word dominion means home which is another way of
> saying care or stewardship—a meaning that I think is more
> in tune with what I'm trying to get at ... whether there are
> threads in the law that embrace a natural commons. Or
> I might reread Robinson Jeffers's* (De Rerum Virtute) ...
> *"All things are full of God ... One light is left us ... the
> immense beauty of the world, not the human world ..." or
> Jim Harrison's "Water" ... "Before I was born I was water
> ... This is a round river and we are her fish who become
> water."* (Saving Daylight) *As for theology, I've been drawn
> to the eighteenth-century Jesuit Jean Pierre de Caussade who
> wrote "divine action cleanses the universe, pervading and*

flowing over all creatures ... God's banner by whose hand earth, air, and water are made divine." (The Sacrament of the Present Moment) *Many indigenous civilizations see spirits in nature.* Then there's Pope Francis's Encyclical on Climate Change and Inequality: On Care for Our Common Home. *After being "unglued" from nature as Margaret Atwood put it in an essay "How Did Christianity Come Unglued from Nature?," maybe humans might be re-gluing themselves to nature's kinship. Ethically, it seems more apparent than ever that community, individual, nature, and ethics are inseparable. Aldo Leopold said, "[t]he landowner has an obligation to manage land in the interest of community, as well as his own interest."* (A Sand County Almanac) *What I'm trying to do is find a way within the principles of law to honor the natural order of things ...*

If not, the law of property would not embrace the environment, nature, or the existence of earth itself. Do people, the law, and courts have to wait for the earth to become so damaged by catastrophic events—fires, floods, landslides, deaths from heat, the collapse of public drinking water sources or systems? Do courts have to accept a legal fate, to the extent of righteous rigidity, that there's no way back?

Or is there a point at which the burden of proof shifts to keep open the opportunity for a way back? Those who seek to alter the natural order would need to show that what they want to do will not impair or destroy the patterns and nature of this natural order, in an ontological sense. In this way, the law would retain the attributes of the adversarial process in its search for truth, justice, and fairness and, at the same time, embrace respect for the presence of this ontological existence—nature and values beyond the status quo of seeing things and people only as mere atomistic objects.

It follows that the law should shift from a purely "rights-based" system to a "respect-rights" based one. The compound word "respect-rights" would mean that nature and human relationships to nature, not just to each other, would become part of the status quo—which, in the end, is undeniable. So, this natural order or ontological essence cannot be changed or altered without the person seeking the change proving that such change would not impair or destroy its special value and its relationship to the natural order and the viability of this order. By placing rights in the context of a respect-rights-based system, under certain circumstances, the burden of proof shifts—a way courts and humanity can assure that the pattern that connects the whole is not irreparably damaged.

But experience shows that human nature is not so charitable or cooperative as it could be. I would guess that most of us wake up every day and hear about yet another catastrophe or collapse of this or that and sense there's something wrong. But we still shop for discounts, online or otherwise, goods made at the expense of someone or something else so we can consume more as if the natural world has no limits. We drive, fly, burn, consume literally like there is no tomorrow. There is also a nexus here to the idea that free markets define reality, so-called neoliberalism, because it substitutes markets for regulation of the transactional nature of property as a commodity without recognition of the harm or interference with common property in which the whole people are interested. It seems equally true that the promotion of justice for an interest in which the whole people are interested must be paramount to the business of a free-market economics which has no room for the extent of its collateral damage.

I have to say something at this point about myself, my background. Otherwise, this dissent could be misunderstood as the opinion of a tree-hugging liberal or anti-capitalist or socialist. I'm not. I'm a trained lawyer and a judge; I grew up in a family of businesspeople. My dad, gone for twenty years now, owned and ran a boom and bust small auto-parts factory before the auto giants moved production and jobs to the sunbelt and overseas. He was an avid outdoors person and bird lover—he never missed a December bird count for Audubon, shoving me into red-plaid snowpants and parka, and rowing us out to his duck blind in the middle of a nearly frozen coastal swamp full of creeks, seeps, open water, buttressed cedars, an eagle's nest perched on the tip of a ghostlike trunk, and a few towering lonesome pines.

My mother, along with part-time interior decorating work for customers of a furniture store, raised us along with a vegetable garden to feed us. "You must understand someday we may need seeds and know how to grow our own food," she'd say. Hard work, family dinner around a table with a tablecloth, silverware, napkins, water glasses, nothing fancy, nothing wasted, the fifties and sixties thing until the collapse of Camelot, the decade of assassinations … riots over racism, Vietnam War, 1968 Chicago convention … I'm digressing. My point is I'm struggling in writing this dissent. Private property, capital, jobs, taxes, all that have for a long time brought about good for our stability, safety, and welfare, our communities. But sometime, I don't know when, capitalism became imprisoning … not concerned with the middle class or poor person, but financial gain … not the economy envisioned by the early free-market economists like Hayek and Friedman. I thought they railed against planned economies that killed creativity and innovation in backrooms, garages, shops, small labs, and backstreets—think of Edison, Carver, Whitney, Granville Woods, the Wright Brothers, Martha Stewart, Detroit's James Vernor, Motown Records, Marie Van Brittan Brown, Yvon Chouinard—the list never ends. You can add the whole Silicon Valley's inventors and bosses, a boiling pot of boggling technology, although it's not clear where it's "new technology at all costs" mentality is any different than someone removing a rare dune. As I noted before, what's the difference between government and corporate-controlled economies? They both control and plan the economy to benefit an elite few … I studied law in Detroit ten years after the 1967 riots when the city erupted from decades of racism and poverty, red-lined mortgages so whites could control who owned and lived where, the property, the corporate flight to the suburbs, abandoning Detroit and its people to miles and miles of boarded-up, burned-out wasteland. As you can gather, creativity and entrepreneurial innovation go together. But this free-market or neoliberal ideology has poisoned the law and society so much so that the only law you need to know is the law of "free markets."

Maybe property ownership and rights of entitlement and extraction from nature and others have gone "too far" in the same way that regulation of property can go "too far" when there is a denial of fairness and justice and the takings of private property. There was a decision brought by the Supreme Court (another mining case) that a state's code that prohibited mining coal near or under adjacent land to prevent subsidence to neighbors took away the mining company's property right to mine. The decision ignored the property of neighbors in favor of mining. The Court, ironically Justice Holmes, ruled that depriving the coal company of its right to its reserved rights to minerals under the surface of the land went "too far." You can look it up: Pennsylvania Coal Company v Mahon. I have ruminated to the point of futility over this case, first because it is a mining case like this one, second because Justice Holmes never harmonized his ruling with his observation that rivers and waters escape a lawyer's view with the coal company's severed mineral rights, he considered more important than the damage to the lands of neighbors and the community. What if the mining caused subsidence of land near a lake or a river? There are distinctions of course, public waters and the like, and I suppose he may have looked at the neighbors and community's interests differently than I am doing here ... Reminds me of Anaconda's copper mine in Butte, Montana. Can someone buy land or mineral rights near or under a city with the expectation it includes the right to destroy it? Again, what if it were a river? Is coal the "great God Progress" now that we know its true cost from climate impacts? But that was a hundred years ago ... This "too far" principle goes both ways. Anyway, I'm not aware of Adam Smith, neoliberalism, or any other unrestrained "free" market system that puts first the common good of the people or earth as a whole. I realize that there are many faces and sides to things in the law, that sometimes it mirrors life and sometimes it doesn't.

This ambivalence over the meaning of property and my role as a judge has put me in a bind. There are sides or cracks in all of us, not just personally, but economically ... We like and detest a thing, action, or belief at the same time. But these two or multi-sides are exploited by education, politics, and media to brainwash us ... There's a legal philosopher who in the 1930s published a book, Law and the Modern Mind. *I had to read it for a jurisprudence class in law school. He challenged the legal system's belief that dogmatic rules assured or resulted in justice in a given case, demonstrating that many factors influenced decisions, especially how court decisions often involved reflection on social impacts. Granted, he wrote this in the middle of the Great Depression but aren't there lessons here about the financial collapse of markets and the grave impact on the millions of people in bread lines, no money, no jobs ... homeless. Today, there's this gnawing, increasing uncertainty about the future as the intensity of unrest and violence seem, more and more, directly connected to the lack of water, food, health care, and social safety nets; not even markets deliver goods in an orderly, timely fashion anymore. We have three branches of government, a fourth I suppose, "We the people." So, what is a judge supposed to do when the legislative and executive branches, the elected officials, fail to address or outright deny or even pass laws, expressly contrary to these social safety nets ... leading to more wildfires and drought, floods, and infrastructure collapse ... eventually more violence to every aspect of our lives ... Am I as a judge a prisoner of the other two branches? Do I do nothing while the other two branches fester ... even draw blood because of entrenched ideological illusions ... delusions. Am I only a utilitarian vessel, or a keeper of value that can't be measured by dollars or public and private economic benefits and costs? Can I as a judge step in when these actions or omissions are contrary to the public health, safety, and general welfare that these officials take an oath to protect and promote? Judges fashion what we call common law, the rulings of courts, which have been dynamic, although slowly responsive, as society comes to grips with the need for justice, fairness, and change. Sure, judges should defer some judgment to a legislature or Congress, but should they when these leaders abdicate or violate their oaths and responsibilities? Reminds me of that Leonard Cohen song about a crack in everything. If sooner or later the mind (or is it mine?) conforms to the truth, isn't it the role of judges and the law to do so as well? Enough said …*

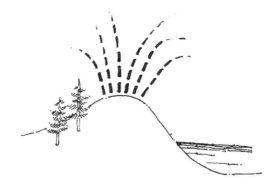

A
SUDDEN BREAK

He had
only four hours ...

$\mathcal{J}$udge Odom felt dizzy, his head felt squeezed by forceps, his synapses snapped off, clicked on, and he fell flat on the floor. He got up, took a deep breath, and looked around his chambers. The text of what he'd written was still on the screen. In the corner the time read 4:33 a.m. He needed water, and something to eat. He picked up a coffee cup and filled it at a drinking fountain in the dimly lit hall. He opened the wood-framed opaque glass doors. He could see the shadows of the leaves from the old elm outside the row of arched windows. He looked toward his bench.

All these years, he realized, he'd never seen the bench from this vantage point. All the lives in crisis, their presence before him more symptom than crime or judgment, all the fights over the meaning of a single word or phrase in a law or regulation, an appellate opinion, a deed. All the fights over property. Over contracts. Child custody and parental rights. Business breakups. Accidents and personal injuries. Environmental wars … Where did they go, where are they now … the parties, lawyers, witnesses, families, organizations, corporations, coalitions? The march of time … the havoc of time … like the case where he'd issued an injunction to save the crown of giant maples over the highway. The state's lawyer said the trees would all be dead and gone in twenty years anyway, so why not cut them now? But that wasn't what mattered. What mattered was the present: the presence and the relationship to these old trees planted by the Civilian Conservation Corps in the 1930s. Conflict, suffering, these are real … the time a defense lawyer argued that a victim dying of cancer from chemical exposure wouldn't suffer much pain and suffering because he didn't have long to live. Did that lawyer learn a lesson!

He took a jar of peanut butter from a small refrigerator kept in his office, grabbed a knife, and spread a gob on a rice cake he removed from a plastic bag in a drawer. It broke into pieces. "Why do these damn things crumble all the time," he murmured as he licked the peanut butter stuck to his fingers. He felt his mind come alive, his opinion shifting, moving again, converging toward a single point in the distance. He glanced at the time again. Five hours to finish. His fingers started typing.

He ate, wiped the crumbs from the desk with his handkerchief, and stretched his arms over his head. He tried to imagine his sculpture of Lady Justice without a blindfold or sword. What had happened, where had he just traveled, where would he end up with this dissenting opinion?

THE DISSENTING OPINION OF
JUDGE ODOM R. HOLMES (CONTINUED)

So, under the common law—the published opinions of judges— is there a background principle that embraces nature beyond the thoughts of the human mind? Based on common experience and knowledge, no one disputes the grandeur and distinctive character of this ten-thousand-year-old dune, a moving sea of sand driven by the physical forces of a rare, global freshwater coastal dune system. But is there a rare or special common property interest that underlies the title to private property? It is my dissenting opinion that the answer is, "Yes." There is a remnant in the law that embraces both public and private property. Under proper circumstances the law recognizes an inherent common property or public interest that springs from the special natural character of the land, water, fauna and flora, or the special cultural relationships regarding people to the land, water, or the earth.

I find that these coastal dunes, including the Voyager Dune, are an ancient, rare, unique commons of an unusual character in which the whole society (the public) is interested. It is my opinion, therefore, insofar as the claim regarding the mound values exist, the burden shifts to Mython to prove the mound and cultural value do not exist. It cannot mine or remove the dune unless it conducts tests, perhaps exploratory efforts with an independent advisor, and proves that the mound does not exist.

The remaining question is whether the law recognizes this public common interest in the alleged mound, or dune, to the extent that it imposes a limitation on the defendant's title and the right to extract from the dune all the sand and profits it desires?

Where do I start? Hundreds of thousands of years ago there was sun, earth, water, sky, plants, and animals. Humans appeared (according to various evolution or creation stories), first as nomadic hunters and gatherers, then small bands, tribes, then herders, following the patterns of nature—the game, herds, seasons. After that came small settlements, then settlers and villages with farming, then cities and civilizations that irrigated the land, and diverted rivers—larger cities, everywhere, then language, words, cultures, customs, written words, printed words, whole civilizations lost to sediments of time ... some dark, some enlightened ... then new cities with trading and commerce spread across the world, and new boundaries, and conflicts, violence, control and power, war, truce, and peace over those boundaries, then nothing, then the gatherers and hunters, wanderers without boundaries returned ... It starts over again as the arcs of generations pass through the world we know as earth. Did God make the world for us, so we get to do whatever we want whenever we desire ... wars ... earth's collapse ... even if it destroys us? Is there another flood, a fire ... The thought creeps in every so often that the "third world war," if we're excluding all the conflict and wars that came before now, is a war to save the planet, we're still fighting old battles ... Is there another way that we can't see?

During the reign of the Emperor Justinian I (528 to 565 CE), fragments of Byzantine laws were codified into Roman Law. One codification stands out: "By the law of nature these things are common to all mankind—the air, running water, the sea, and consequently the shore of the sea."[9] The seashore and riverbanks were considered res communes, or jus publicum. The Roman Empire extended throughout Europe and into the British Isles at the time. By this code and custom, people had access to the shore and banks of rivers for fishing and travel. Not surprisingly, the Magna Carta and the evolution of the common law of England recognized a paramount right of the people to access the banks and waters of navigable rivers and the oceans for their sustenance and survival.

The monarchs of England and Europe owned land and favored the lords of the manors who supported them. Peasants in villages were allowed at the pleasure of the Crown, or the "lord of the manor," to grow food and herd and pasture animals in the meadows and forests as if it were common property. Then the lords invented what we might understand as licenses or leases for those they favored to enjoy preferred rights over other peasants, to manage and promote farming and grazing to increase rents for the manor estate. Over time this closed off soil and meadows from the peasants. So, the more natural boundaries defined by the movements of gatherers, hunters, herders, and peasants' use of the open commons, the more it was settled. It is known as the enclosure movement.[10] Monarchs and those in charge of estates began to enclose the common peasant lands to benefit those in control and the owners. Poorer, less favored peasants were forced to graze their few animals farther and farther away from the manor estate. The peasants were forced to leave the village and land to work in cities for the rising merchant class for a pittance, not much better than remaining on the manor estates. Over time land was measured, bounded, divided, possessed, used, transferred, and traded or sold as private property by instruments of conveyances, what we know as deeds or marketable titles.

....

9   J. Inst. Promeium, 4, 5, 6, Sec. 2.1. A good rendition of this history is found in Blumm and Wood, *The Public Trust Doctrine in Environmental and Natural Resource Law* (Carolina Academic Press, 2013), pp. 12–13.

10 E.g., Karl Widerquist et al., *The Pre-History of Private Property: Implications for Modern Political Theory* (Edinburgh Univ. Press, 2001); Eric Freyfogle, The Enclosure of America, Ill. Research Paper, No. 07-10 (Nov. 2007).

A brief explanation ... By court decision and in some instances new laws, corporations became "persons." For what has turned out to have a profound impact on our democracy, communities, and earth, corporate personhood slipped through the back door of the Supreme Court in a perfunctory order on a request for permission to appeal (it's called a "writ of certiorari"). Without explanation, the Court simply stated in the order that a corporation could be viewed as a "person." Viewed by whom? People? Despite no mind, body, heart, or soul, a corporation became a "person" ... no wonder people today decry this when courts won't recognize living features ... not as fiction ... but as a "person" in the eyes of the law. And corporations were given personhood without oral argument or formal decision by the Court. Corporations started, I suppose, with Sir Francis Drake and the Golden Hind, Sir Walter Raleigh, and the defeat of Spain, Portugal, and the Dutch. In what became the first of many moments of ascension of the British Empire, the Crown chartered the British East India trading company that allowed lords to invest in the venture without liability for anything the company did beyond the person's investment. Global colonization by corporations was born—like the so-called "new world order," I suppose a prescient euphemism for the World Trade Organization today. In 1769, George III "by the grace of God" chartered Dartmouth College as a "body corporate" with the power to acquire land, receive gifts, and transact all other affairs as a "natural person ... is able to do." The college like others at that time was formed for the ministry and Indians according to the "grand design."[11] Not long after the Declaration

....

11 Granted by King George III of Great Britain in 1769, the Charter establishes "a college erected in our said province of New Hampshire by the name of Dartmouth College, for the education and instruction of youth of the Indian tribes in this land in reading, writing, and all parts of learning which shall appear necessary and expedient for civilizing and christianizing children of pagans, as well as in all liberal arts and sciences, and also of English youth and any others." Dartmouth College Charter | Dartmouth Library

of Independence, states started authorizing corporations for private corporate purposes. Soon, as the need to accumulate and manage large sums of money for speculative projects, investments, and profits mounted, nearly anyone could form a corporation, limit personal liability of its investors or stockholders, and seek their financial bonanza without personal responsibility ... I remember when the Supreme Court let lawyers advertise because advertising, spending money for message, constituted protected free speech. I shuddered when as a young lawyer I first read the opinion ... Today, economic speech is at full throttle without any thought ... speech you pay for to persuade another through marketing and promotion for personal or political gain is the same absolute free speech protection under the First Amendment as a real person. The inalienable rights of a human being proclaimed in the Declaration of Independence say nothing about corporate or paid-for speech ... Talk about a slippery slope ... a steep one at that. In a now infamous case decided in 2010 known as Citizens United, *our Supreme Court ruled that political donations constituted protected first amendment "paid-for-political speech." Do corporations really have the same inalienable rights as people, even though their speech costs more than most people can afford? To think all of this fictional personhood of corporations is now mating with artificial intelligence to create a humanity based on a virtual house of cyber bytes and digital cards ... Well, I've wandered beyond the questions on commons and property, but I can't help but think that what I'm touching on here is this idea of absolutism of rights in things, not real persons, that someone can own, like private property, minerals, oil, grain, genetic crops, guns, you name it ... with no concern for the responsibility for collateral damage as the result of such absolutisms ... this includes property, "free" ... it's paid for ... speech, and corporations as "persons" ... Ownership and commodification of the last grain of sand, the last clipped gene, or drop of water are warping reality beyond recognition ...*

It is said that the "chief end" of government is the "preservation of property" as if it is a divine right.[12] No wonder we hear the adage, property is a "sacred cow." The title to private land ownership carries with it three basic rights: exclusive possession to use and enjoy the land free from interference; the right to extract benefit from the land; and the right to convey or exchange between two or more other persons. Traditionally, "property is a closed system, each tract of land or thing separate from the rest of the world."[13]

> *When I think of property, I think of its stability as a function of the power and might of a country behind it. I read once that United States refused to sign the 1982 Convention of the Law of Sea ... I think it was the Secretary of Navy under President Reagan who said the U.S. opposed the treaty because it limited corporate mining of seabeds, and, true to his tough cold-war views, he said something like, "We don't need the treaty, if we need something, we've got the power to get it." Isn't this our history, using a beguiling divine right to decimate forests and tribal civilizations? Today's extreme expectations of property have little relationship to the ownership of our home or the earth's commons.[14]*

Some courts view these property rights as absolute rights to use or extract no matter the harm. Because of filth, deterioration, and disease from the rise of industry in the late 1800s, by the early 1900s governments started regulating these activities to prevent harm and

....

12 Andrew McLaughlin, *A Constitutional History of the United States* (Appleton-Century-Crofts, 1936), Chapter X, pp. 92–95.

13 John Locke, *Second Treatise on Civil Government* (1689).

14 Standing behind the "title" to property in the United States is a church-backed principle adapted by European monarchies known as the "discovery doctrine." This tragic doctrine was used to justify European occupancy, settlement and ownership that displaced and destroyed tribal civilizations in non-Christian lands, because the millennial occupancy and settlement didn't conform to the standards of the Christian world. E.g., Johnson v McIntosh, 2 1 U.S. 543 (1823).

promote the public good under the more progressive leadership of Taft and later President Roosevelt.

> *This makes me think of another case that is worth comparing. In Cedar Point Nursery v Hassid, the court said a law excusing union representatives from trespassing so they could go on farms to talk to workers constituted a taking of private property.[15] Yet, in the famous Penn Central Station historic preservation case,[16] the Court protected the historical values of the station by upholding a city regulation that prohibited development of the airspace above the station. Boosted by ethical and community values, it said that "[t]he landowner has an obligation to manage land in the interest of community, as well as his own interest." (Aldo Leopold,* A Sand County Almanac *and* Sketches Here and There) *Again, Pope Francis in his* Encyclical on Climate Change *and from the depths of his meditations urges this for an impoverished world: "[T]he environment is a collective good ... the responsibility of everyone," and the "common good" is an "ethical imperative," "we can no longer view reality in a purely utilitarian way ... geared entirely for our individual benefit ..." or Wendell Berry's* Another Turn of the Crank. *But since then, regulations have been marginalized because they interfere with free markets and the rights of property. Czeslaw Milosz nailed it with these lines in his "Diary of a Naturalist": "We were flying over a range of snow peaked mountains / And throwing dice for the soul of the condor / —Should we grant reprieve to the condor? / —No, we won't grant reprieve to the condor / It didn't eat from the tree of Knowledge and so it must perish. / ...Fare well, Nature / Fare well, Nature." There's no end to references that attest to these higher values. As Kurt Vonnegut put it, "We'll go down in history as the first society that wouldn't save itself because it wasn't cost-effective. Or wasn't profitable. The way things*

---

15   141 S. Ct. 2063 (2021).

16   Penn Central v New York City, 438 U. S. 104 (1978).

are going, maybe the last." Without flaming swords at the gate of Eden, we humans are cooked ... now we're going after the "tree of life" itself. If I were an artist, I'd paint a big mural, billboard size, with earth nailed to a crossbar.

But note the contrast I just made by the word "regulation" as opposed to an outright limitation on the rights of private property. Even Locke and his ilk recognized, long since ignored, that these rights are subject to mutual preservation for the public good. And this remains so—the U.S. Supreme Court noted that a limitation on the exercise of a property right to a dune on the shore of the ocean is not a taking of a private property if there is a legally recognized background public interest or limitation under our judge-made common law.[17] The *Lucas* case stated that no compensation is owed to a landowner if the limitation "inheres in the title itself, in the restrictions that background principles of the State's law of property and nuisance already place upon land ownership."[18]

The Supreme Court decided there's no background principle where a state can authorize union organizers to trespass on private farms to talk to farmworkers. But this doesn't help any, because affirmatively authorizing someone to invade your property would legalize trespass ... except where there's a war, emergency of life or limb, or criminal conduct and you have a warrant ... Because background principles that protect commons and community are a limitation, not an active intrusion. Sure, a regulation can deny all use of property and run afoul of the constitution, but what about where there is present an inherent special common value like lakes, streams, or other property of a special character? As Aldo Leopold put it in the footnote I mentioned above, there is a limitation on the use of private property where it invades the "interest of community." It should be noted that even free-market gurus, like Richard Epstein in Principles for a

....

17   Lucas v South Carolina Coastal Council, 505 U.S. 1003 (1992).

18   Id.

Free Society, *recognized that the individual liberty and the rights of private property were limited where necessary for the common good, including the law of common property and custom.*

* * *

Back to the remaining question in this dissent: Aside from the claimed mound, is there a common law or background principle that embraces nature as Yeats puts it, beyond the thoughts of the human mind that limits the defendant Mython's property right to mine the Voyager Dune?

Land, water, the earth, plants, animals, including us humans are bound by law and political power to enforce property and the property rights that go with land ownership—what we call real property law. As mentioned earlier, real property law came down through the centuries to each state from what was once considered land owned by the monarchs and used by people in common at the pleasure of a monarch. Then it was enclosed or controlled commons, and then, finally, property—described, circumscribed, assignable, exclusive private rights that became a cornerstone for the accumulation of wealth extracted from the land, without regard for impacts to others beyond the boundaries of the property. Yet threads can be found in the common law that also recognized rights in land and water of a special character or feature that was considered common property. This was because water is for the most part incapable of ownership and critical for survival. As nineteenth-century jurist Thomas Cooley put it, "water is a movable, wandering thing, must of necessity continue common by the law of nature."[19] What other lands or natural features might be incapable or partly incapable of wholly private ownership because of their special character and customs and cultural relationships to them?

Historically, some lands and waters have been considered common to all, and still are, perhaps more so as world popu-

---

19 *Blackstone*, Vol I, Chap. 2, p. 16.

lation pushes past eight billion, global temperatures set new records every year, stock markets rise faster than heat, tensions and violence break out in a cacophony of divisive ideology and, perhaps, a hopeless, fatalistic uncertainty. I remember driving with my wife, Harriet, on I-94 west of Minneapolis to visit Yellowstone and Glacier National Parks. We heard a muffled crack outside, the sound of a branch snapping. When I looked in the rearview mirror pieces of a turtle's shell floated in the backwind of the car. I shuddered when I recalled that Lakotas saw North America as a turtle … I don't know why I'm mentioning this, only that when I saw the bits of shell, I had this foreboding feeling about humanity speeding into the future … As Kurt Vonnegut said in A Life, *"So, it goes." I hope not.*

* * *

After the American Revolution, each state became a sovereign, meaning a government of its people, not crowned kings or queens, including the passing down of English common law to the new and later admitted states of this country. In 1821, the New Jersey Supreme Court had to decide whether a citizen who took oysters from the exposed seabed trespassed on the seabed in front of a shoreline of a landowner's property who grew and claimed ownership of the oysters. The court answered, "No," noting there are three kinds of property: (1) private property; (2) the public domain or property owned by the government as landowner (think capitol buildings, highways, parks, state and national forests); and (3) common public property owned by a state as sovereign for its people—a "gift of nature … destined for the common health, use, enjoyment of every individual citizen."[20] So, each colony that became a state and every state that

---

20 Arnold v Mundy, 6 N.J. 1 at 49-50. The ruling recognized a legally enforceable stewardship principle that was embedded in common public property or property in which the whole of a society have an interest. As far as I have found, this is the bedrock law in every state and the United States Supreme Court. So is the U.S. Supreme Court case Shively v Bowlby, 152 U.S. 1, 11 (1894), vesting title to navigable waters and the lands beneath them in each

entered the Union after that became vested with title to the navigable waters and the lands under them. Is public common property limited to water and the land under it? Or, put another way, are other public common property or interests "gifts of nature" in which the whole people are interested?

In 1892, in a celebrated case known as Illinois Central Railroad v Illinois, the Supreme Court considered the validity of a conveyance by the state legislature of about one-square mile of the lakebed under Lake Michigan to a railroad company for a large transportation and shipping complex on Chicago's waterfront.[21] After an outcry from some of Chicago's most influential families and a resounding public campaign to stop it, the legislature repealed the conveyance. The railroad company refused to concede its ownership, and the dispute ended up in the Supreme Court. The Court ruled that all navigable waters and the land under them were owned by a state in trust for its citizens for fishing and navigation, and cited the 1821 New Jersey case. The Court nixed the conveyance because under the common law the state did not have the right to convey exclusive private property rights in the public waters and lakebed. Today, any title or right in land under a navigable lake or river is subject to the paramount common or public right of citizens for fishing, navigation, swimming, boating, sustenance, and other essential public needs; these principles are known as the Public Trust Doctrine.[22] Even a private

---

state held in trust for its citizens for fishing, navigation, sustenance, and other essential needs. More recently, the Court reaffirmed states' title and the trust principle in PPL Montana v Montana, 565 U.S. 576 (2012).

21 Illinois Central R Rd v Illinois, 146 U.S. 387 (1892); Joseph L. Sax, The Public Trust Doctrine in Natural Resources Law, 68 Mich L. Rev. 471 (1970); for a well-researched history of the Illinois Central case, see Joseph Kearney and Thomas Merrill, *Lakefront: Public Trust and Private Rights in Chicago* (Cornell University Press, 2021).

22 Id.; for current background on the public trust doctrine, see Michael Blumm and Mary Christina Wood, *The Public Trust Doctrine in Environmental and Natural Resources Law* (Carolina Academic Press, 2013); Mary Christina Wood, *Nature's Trust* (Cambridge University Press, 2013). For a stricter interpretation of the doctrine, see James Huffman, "The Public Trust Doctrine: A Brief (and True) History," 10 George Washington J. E. & Env. L. 15 (2019).

owner's title or property interest in the land under an inland lake or a stream is limited by the right of the people to use this special common public property for these public trust uses.[23] No one, neither the state nor person can subordinate or diminish the public rights to enjoy these protected uses of this special common property. Like the beneficiaries to a trust managed by a bank, citizens as beneficiaries have a right to force the trustee to protect the trust property and their rights.

Mython argues, understandably, that these common property and public trust principles apply only to the submerged lands under navigable water. The People of the Dune argues that there is an inherent common property or public interest that limits or qualifies Mython's rights to remove the upland dunes. The Mound People Coalition argues that Mython's exclusive right to mine the dune would risk the loss of deep cultural relationships with a remnant mound from a previous civilization that inhabited the Great Lakes region. As noted above, land came to the states as property under common law. But at the same time the ownership of the water and the land beneath passed to each state as a public commons subject to the principles of the public trust doctrine. Upland passed to this country as private property with defined property rights of the owner—individually owned, distinct, exclusive, exploitable, and transferrable.

> *Years ago, I had a zoning case involving an ordinance that limited the transferability of a planned unit shopping center unless approved by a township board. The new developer's lawyer relied on an oft-cited law review article that argued land is "a commodity affected with a public interest." I found this odd, because the law has always viewed land and its use as unique and different from a commodity, enough so that recovering damages for injury to land cannot compensate for the unique rights and features associated with land.*

---

23 Collins v Gerhardt, 237 Mich 38 (1926); A landowner couldn't kick a fisherman out of the stream that ran through his property; McMorran Milling Co. v C. H. Little Co., 201 Mich 301 (1918); the right of the landowner to mine sand and gravel from his riverbed was qualified by the rights of the public to navigate and fish.

As Will Rogers observed, "Buy land. They ain't making any more of the stuff." No matter who owns land or water, they are finite, and nonrenewable ... I wondered: had society reached a point where land was nothing different than a box of cereal or a slab of beef? I ruled the township could regulate the transferability of the shopping center because the township had an interest in assuring the public health, safety, and welfare of its citizens.

✴ ✴ ✴

But what makes property common? Water, that's easy; no one owns water, only a right to use it. But the Supreme Court in the Chicago waterfront case left the door open for other public common property or interests: "The state can no more abdicate its title to property in which the whole people are interested, *like* navigable waters and the soils under them ... than it can abdicate the police powers [of government]," and then concluded, "So with trusts *connected with public property, or property of a special character, like* lands under navigable waters, they cannot be placed entirely beyond the control of the state" (the italics are mine). In plain language, the opinion leaves the door open for courts, a judge, to rule that land or natural features, even if not under navigable water, could be declared common property or common interest in property that is held in public trust for the public. If the plain meaning of words in context is understood to be intended, there's no quibble. The court used the word "like" twice, meaning that water is just one example of what may be common property, and then described this special character as a trust connected with "public property, or property of a special character." So, the door is open for me, under the right circumstances, to find that Voyager Dune is common property of a "special character" "in which the whole people are interested."

Some fifty years ago, a hotel chain wanted to expropriate the mouth of a river that flowed through the town where I live and into a bay on Lake Michigan. It riled neighborhoods and budding environmentally minded residents who used the area for swimming and picnicking, so much so that they filed a lawsuit. The residents claimed that the river mouth constantly changed from natural forces over the years, that what was upland became submerged and what was submerged became upland, and that it was of a unique special character like the adjacent waters and submerged lands. The circuit judge (long before I became judge) ruled that a public trust could attach to upland property where a river joined the waters of a bay and while in public hands was used by citizens as a beach, swimming, and for fishing. However, after trial, the judge found against the residents because he didn't think the property had a sufficiently distinctive character; it was my impression that judge was influenced overall because after he allowed the claim to proceed to trial, the hotel developer redesigned the hotel perpendicular to the shore, leaving a portion of the beach open and useable by residents.[24] Too, courts often protect parklands as dedicated common property or protected by this public trust doctrine. When I reread the Arnold v Mundy case, cited by the People of the Dune Coalition, it dawned on me that there is a thread in the common law that recognizes private property is superordinate to common property or natural features of a special character and value to the community as a whole.

How does this background principle of common property hold up under the lens of our history, ethics, and values? I take judicial notice that the connection of humans to the earth and environment is undisputed. Our sciences—geology, hydrology, biology, climatology, and ecology, etc.—have confirmed this connection. As Gregory Bateson warned, "destroy quality and you destroy the pattern that connects."

This is the premise of Gregory Bateson's book Mind and Nature. *The irony of Bateson's patterns of connection*

---

24 See Taxpayers in the Public Interest v Department of State Highways and Northern Michigan Inns, Grand Traverse County Cir. Ct. No. 3137, Opinion, Hon. William Brown, Cir. Judge, May 3, 1973.

between humans and nature (or public common services like education) in the 1970s is that in 1980 the country elected a populist Hollywood star as president who stood for just the opposite. After a decade of new bipartisan laws and court decisions that held the promise of restraining humanity's heavy foot on the environment, earth, and people, President Reagan led a charge to dismantle those laws in the name of deregulation and free markets—so-called "trickle-down economics." This makes me think of Robert Pirsig's characters' quests for quality, Zen and the Art of Motorcycle Maintenance, *and later values, in his book* Lila—*the narrators' quest for values led him to the present moment that the molecules of the air began to move just milliseconds ahead of a speeding train ... Like many I suppose, I related to the narrator's quest when I read* Motorcycle Maintenance *in college ... the narrator cycling west with his son and his desperate self. ... Maybe I'm getting into regrets of the past, not a wise thing to do at my age. I had the urge to do something ... off to hike Europe or South America like so many other coming-of-age journeys. But I saw it rationally, like the urges would pass, and then I was in law school, then met my wife, Harriet, married, children ... we all go through passages, sometimes duties that feel like ruts, sometimes without duty, just expression of self or a dream ... I mean, when I became a judge at thirty-nine, the wild urges, trips, the regrets for experiences that weren't lived, gave way to a different quest ... something about finding yourself ... or more than that ... acceptance, giving in to the choices made that defined the conditions of one's life in the presence of every moment ... It was about the same time that an artist friend sensed that art was in the middle of a courtroom battle between a highway and a river. Is art to the law the same as Robert Pirsig's art is to the maintenance of a motorcycle? Who knows? A straight line isn't as straight as it appears. Everything is curved and turning in, out, inward, outward ... inside out, outside in ... hopefully, all rising or spiraling upward toward some kind of higher good ... a mystery not of our doing ...*

In the past fifty years, some economists have come to grips with the realization that traditional economics fails to account for the reality of the external punishment and damage inflicted on humans, other species, and the vital common interests of the natural world. The effect of human behavior on every aspect of soil, water, and the life cycles of plants, animals, and humans has gone beyond the reality of its own natural boundaries. It seems now that it may exceed our own capacity for resilience to survive.

I hope not … Albeit dark, do we need any more proof of the connection between humans and earth? This leads me back to the garden and flaming swords that protect the tree of life … What was it Bateson said, something like … "it was us humans who kicked God out of the garden?" A few years back I read a book called The Invention of Nature. *I realized as I read this book that Bateson and others, such as Pope Francis in his* Encyclical on Climate Change and Inequality, *stand on the shoulders of an extensive line of scientists, explorers, philosophers, poets, conservationists, theologians, and mystics. Wulf uncovers the prescient views of nineteenth-century Prussian explorer-scientist Alexander von Humboldt whose perilous world wanderings led to his observation that "nature was a reflection of the whole." As Wulf reveals, von Humboldt's wanderings and meticulous writings rippled through his country and around the world, resonating with poets, scientists, and leaders—Goethe, Darwin, Jefferson, Thoreau, Marsh, Hickel, John Muir … more recently the likes of Bateson, Leopold, and E.O. Wilson … and before and since many more men and women (those I mentioned earlier) who also challenged the human order of things by abandoning to the true nature of the experience of the seen and unseen world. To reject this is to deny reality, which if the law refuses to embrace, would deny justice. I read Herman Daly's* Steady-State Economics *after I heard him speak at a forum on property, economics, and the environment in the late 1980s, about the damage not accounted for by the measures of classical economics. Four decades later the systemic environmental harm and climate crisis have slammed us so hard it's not clear whether we can shift our economic paradigm in time. Daly seemed to have a deep faith, spiritually but also in opportunity, which to me points yet again to the pattern of connections between faith, nature, and people. Years ago, I heard a man who had dedicated his life to living and working according to the economics defined by the natural order of things—he left activism and managed a thousand-acre forest—speak to a group of environmentalists, educators, and religious leaders. "The earth is one vast self-regulating, self-organizing, healing organism," he said. As a Jesuit retreat master once said in a deep, peaceful voice to a group of us retreatants, "Sooner or later the mind conforms to the truth." Oh, my ...*

Political scientist and Nobel Prize winner Elinor Ostrom has shown that respecting common pooled resources means that traditional economics and Hardin's "tragedy of the commons," the competition to extract earth's commons for profit with unredeemable destruction, are not unchangeable or inevitable.[25]

Maybe we sapiens aren't imprisoned by complex dualities or splits from reality after all ... I remember watching Ostrom on TV when she accepted the Nobel Prize in economics. Her message gave me shivers ... She had spent a lifetime watching human problem-solving behaviors, and discovered and proved that human behavior will accept cooperation to manage and protect common resources over violence, if given a choice. As a judge, I hear conflicts and make decisions based on the law. But this has also involved nudging litigants and attorneys that come before me in an adversarial process, sometimes a verbal, mental fistfight, like the one I'm addressing in this opinion. The adversary process does an excellent and important job identifying differences, issues, and getting a better picture of the truth through cross-exam-

....
25 Elinor Ostrom, *Governing the Commons* (Cambridge University Press, 2015).

ination of witnesses and opposing evidence—the more infor-
mation, investigation, probing, the better ... The adversary
process can by its vortex open eyes above the level of the fight
over issues. Sometimes the adversary vortex is a window ...
a glimpse of common ground. But when a case goes to trial,
it's "winner take all." One of Ostrom's principles strikes me
apropos here: "Match rules governing use of common goods
to local needs and conditions" and "... [a]ction by govern-
ments and nongovernmental organizations should enhance
rather than replace social capital, which has been built up at
the community level over generations." (https://dlc.dlib.indi-
ana.edu/dlc/handle/10535/891.) So, determining where
private property ends and a common or community interest
begins is based in part on significant customs and culture of
people where they live. This leads me back again to the law
(adversary process included) as experience ... How can pri-
vate property run contrary to the reality that land and water
is not only property, but the experience of people, their com-
munity, their relationship to nature ... or even nature itself?

The tribes in this case and their members testified that they live
in mutual relationship to the commons of nature. The same may be
true for ethics. As Aldo Leopold said, "[t]he landowner has an obligation to manage land in the interest of community ..."

I'm getting outside the law ... or maybe not ... but the
same may be true spiritually. It just occurred to me that
we've lost sight of what is sacred when it comes to prop-
erty. Is private ownership the "sacred cow" or is it the land,
water, air, the moving features and life on this earth that
are sacred? When the sacred cow real property starts chewing
the earth into a state of systemic collapse, as many scien-
tists and writers warn, it doesn't look very sacred. After all,
didn't God declare upon creation the earth and all that is in
it "good?" De Caussade, whom I mentioned earlier, wrote,
"under God's banner by whose hand earth, air, and water
are made divine." Buddhists see nature as friend, a relation-

ship. Hindus see the divine and nature as one. Han Shan saw nature as reality and spiritual force: "I rest my head happily on a stone pillow and follow the changes of heaven and earth."[26] I read once where Australia's original people lived along "song-lines" as they moved about to follow the water, animals, and plants. The ancient Sami people who still move in summer and winter according to the seasons and pathways of reindeer migrations ... The Maori people who are the original people of New Zealand see nature as family, living beings. It is often said that the ancient Sami people, who can be traced back eight thousand years to what we now call Lapland, when asked where they are from, say, "I'm not from anywhere." They had valleys, mountains, rivers, and the lowlands as they followed the reindeer on which they survived—the boundaries of their life defined by the reindeer, not the bounded ownership of the place. But when civilization is stripped away, maybe we're all from similar origins ... even now, but we just don't know it. The tribal witnesses in this dune case testified to similar effects; they don't see land, a tree, fish, a plant as property, but as relationship. Parenthetically, it seems to me this public trust doctrine I described earlier also recognizes or shields the trust relationship between the government as trustee, the water or natural resource and land of a special character, and the use of these special water and natural resources or land by all citizens as beneficiaries of the trust or fundamental needs.

So, this common property, or commons in nature that preexists the appearance of humans and continues in all that for purposes of this opinion, civilizations and eventually the law of private property of the trust onto nature like a branding iron burns ownership on the hide of a steer. There's the need for security, shelter, food, water, and land, and then community. But for many today, there is no security, no hope, no community. Yet for others it couldn't be better: They can

---

26 No. 241.

do whatever they want no matter what the cost, including the cost to this commons in nature and life itself.

> *I suppose that is so even if it masticates a mountain top into coal or uranium mines, drains the Aral Sea, leaves gadgets and bones on Mt. Everest, a nutrient "dead zone" in Lake Erie or the Gulf of Mexico, scars across the earth the size of Florida to extract more fossil fuels to burn up the planet even faster.*

Private property is a cornerstone for society—security of home, possessions, enjoyment, rest, endeavors, innovation, in short to use the land and its fruits wisely. But to be secure on one's private land, to use its fruits for home, enjoyment, or endeavor, is not to warrant the owner's right to turn the land, water, or nature itself into a product with impunity, certainly not without regard to the damage to common interests of others or the people as a whole.

I conclude that private property is and remains subject to an inherent paramount (meaning "above all else") interest in this commons of nature on which property and all life depend; the existence and paramount nature of the commons is measured by the uniqueness and special character of the common interest in the property in question, and it includes the existence of a substantial cultural relationship consistent with the natural order of things. This commons in land and water (on which the human construct of private property is superimposed) by its nature moves like a timeless river, giving the commons in which all are interested in certain instances a paramount value that temper extreme legal expectations associated with the rights of private property. According to the testimony, in this case coastal dunes shift and move inland in waves (if one hundred years of shifting dunes were compressed into a year, dunes would move not unlike water).

* * *

So, it is undeniable that private property rights depend on these commons. Otherwise, the idea that private property is a fixed, unchanging legal universe of immutable entitlements and rights, a thing unto itself, has led and will lead, inevitably, to the destruction of nature, earth's commons, and untold, incomprehensible suffering for humankind and the other species with whom we share this planet.

> *I won't go into the implications of where the earth is headed with the desires and necessities of another billion people, whether destined or fated, whether apocalypse or a heaven here or on some other plane. I'm dealing with the reality we have right here and now ... the people and organizations and the coastal dunes before me in this case ... not just that ... all of us and those to come ... for whom it's not looking like things are going to get better ...*

This is not without parallels in the world of property and law. Take art, cultural heritage, or original works of literature. As Joe Sax, a pioneer in the law of the commons in nature and cultural values, asked: did the Rockefellers have the right to destroy Diego Rivera's mural in the Modern Museum of Art, exposing the dark side, misery, and horrible conditions of the workers of the world?[27] Sax, in his exploration of cultural commons, suggests the answer is "No." He gave a number of other compelling examples to sharpen the inquiry. For example, when a man shot up his Toulouse-Lautrec painting, the principle droit moral—that "artists retain a continuing interest in their work after it is sold"—was enough to protect the integrity of Lautrec's reputation.[28] Why not nature? If creativity and art spring from or depend on nature in all of its manifestations, why not nature itself?

> *Why not, indeed? Doesn't the artist, the creator, retain an interest in her or his art after it is sold and owned by another, even a stranger? If a human creation in the arts*

....
27 See Joseph Sax's (the same Professor Sax who gave a rebirth to the public trust doctrine, read by so many, now underpinning this opinion) *Playing Darts with a Rembrandt* (University of Michigan Press, 1999). Professor Sax unearthed events surrounding art, history, architecture, and literature that call into question what unbridled private property ownership means.

28 Id., p. 27, n. 1.

carries with it some recognition greater than the exclusive right to the property itself, shouldn't the creation of earth and the universe and its continuing viability be more so? Does the continuing force that created the universe—Creator, "big bang," or magnum mysterium—have a fundamental interest a priori in the earth, its land, water, and nature that is paramount to private property? Is this a way of thinking about drawing a line that limits the demands on private property and leaves open the protection of those public commons of a special character?

Common property springs from the special or unique nature of things that run wild, flow, and move over, in, through our earth and hydrosphere. As the nineteenth-century jurist Cooley wrote, "Water is a moveable, wandering thing … common by the law of nature." Nature is dynamic, not fixed or static. The commons and the legal rights of private property are and always have been in constant tension with nature and the larger cultural values connected to nature. As indicated above, isn't it obvious that private property at some point would no longer have value, economic or otherwise, without the preservation of special commons as a whole? The law is not just a legal construct and reason at the cost of everything else; it is reason, experience, art, quality, value, ultimately tied to a respect for the beingness of things—that is, unless humanity wants to keep waging war against itself. Some think it inevitable, and as indicated earlier, it seems more so every day that the end is already here; that it is too late to respect or conform to the reality or the truth of this natural order.

I remember when President Reagan's Secretary of Interior, Jimmy Watts, infamously said, "We don't have to protect the environment, the Second Coming is at hand." Coincidentally, Jimmy Watts was a lawyer who pitched and fought for the extraction industries. What relevance is there in such a dark apologetics for the demise of the earth and its people when it comes down to our relationship, care, and love for our neighbors? I realize it's difficult, if ever, for any of us that we must succumb or be subject to drawing a line on ourselves and the use of our land. But it now appears the natural order or beingness of things demands this of us.

The preservation of the value of property of a special or unusual character—private or public—is essential to sustain the natural order of things. In my opinion this is also consistent with preservation of private property: as demonstrated through what I think adheres to my duty to honor the principles that underlie binding legal precedent, I reach this conclusion through law, experience, and (as best I can inform myself) the natural order of things—the existence of the Voyager Dune, the mining, private property, and cultural relationships to this coastal dune system and an alleged mound in the case before me. This ontological existence of the commons of nature is—in a sense—a natural encumbrance that is embedded in an owner's land its bundle of rights to exploit with impunity. This is not metaphor or legalism; it is reality.

My thoughts on the law and my non-relation Justice Oliver Holmes and the discussion of ontology touch upon being-ness of nature, humans, and all things ... even God or the Mystery of Creation ... and the earlier references to Pope Francis's Encyclical, de Caussade, or, if not spiritually then on the science side, legal principles must embrace the consequences of human conduct like mining or climate change on the ontological natural order of things.

*   *   *

I hereby hold, meaning it is my ruling, that the plaintiffs in this case, the People of the Dune and Mr. Creek and the Mound People Coalition (the tribes), have stated legally valid claims. The law embraces that nature's commons, which is water, wildlife, air, and land shown to be of a special character or rare and unique, are embedded with an inherent interest in the land, water, plants, the animals that are paramount to the rights of the private property and landowner. The doctrine and the evolution of the law of property, informed by the reality of experience and the natural order of things, recognizes the thread in the common law that protects those instances in which there is a paramount common interest in the special common property of the whole of the people.

> I'm relying on the principles of the long line of cases mentioned throughout this opinion: Arnold v Mundy and its notion of "common property," Illinois Central Railroad and its "common property of a special character, like navigable waters," decisions extending this to tributary non-navigable streams, to tributary groundwater, even land use decisions that affect the public trust in water, the eastern parkland cases in Professor Sax's 1970 Michigan Law Review article, and the Chicago parkland cases. The law is built upon the reality of experience is dynamic, not just logic. This allows me to conclude that plaintiffs have stated a claim that there is inherent limitation on the right to remove or even mine the mound and the dune. Some academics and judges might take a narrower view of commons and public trust law; others would point to a much broader foundation for application of public trust law and a public property commons that I have reached in writing this opinion (see my footnote references on the public trust doctrine). I believe I have established in principle a basis for my ruling in this case that falls well within the lens of these views. At this point, I don't see another way forward, given where humanity's current trajectory is headed.

The property rights of landowners are limited and qualified to the extent that the exercise of those rights if carried out would substantially impair the viability of the special common property in question, necessarily from generation to generation. The law recognizes that the plaintiffs in this case are entitled to a day in court, a full trial on these questions: whether the mound exists, and whether the Voyager Dune is common property of a special character that would be impaired by the proposed mining and removal of the dune. For these reasons and the reality and fact, a fact no one has disputed, that the Voyager Dunes are of an unusual character and rare or unique, I rule that the defendant Mython World Mining Corporation cannot mine and remove, or destroy, the Voyager Dune based on their proposed project unless there is a trial and Mython proves there is no mound, the dune is not a commons of a special character, or that the special character of the dunes that exists will not be impaired.

> *What does a judge do when he dissents from him or herself? However, many sides, planes, angles, or arcs to his or her brain there may be, they must decide as best they can. As any divided court might do, I've had to meet in conference with my self, so to speak, and hash it out. That I have. There's no choice ... these many angles and arcs after all underlie where I've been these past few days. Because a line of precedent based on the values at stake in this case leaves the door open for a court in the right case to find property of a special character is a commons that by its nature and human experience should not be wholly destroyed, I could flat out reverse my Bench Opinion and Order, but that leaves nothing in between. I am not suggesting compromise, how could either side of my brain live with each side or angle still fighting the other? Incidentally, when an appellate court evenly splits, the arguments of the person appealing becomes the ruling of the court .... That aside, here's what I've decided to do ...*

Therefore, my decision three days ago is hereby modified as follows:

There must be a trial to determine whether any amount of mining or development can occur without impairing the special essence of the mound and without impairing the special character of the Voyager Dune and rare coastal dune system of which it is a part.

The claims of the plaintiffs are not dismissed; their claims are scheduled for a trial on whether and to what extent the defendant's extraction can occur without impairing the viability and very essence of what makes Voyager Dune a rare and special natural commons.

154

The burden of proof is on the defendant to establish that there
is no mound, the dune is not a commons of a special character, and the dunes and commons, if proven to exist, will
not be impaired by its mining, removal of the dune, and the
proposed village and residential lakeshore development.

As a matter of law, private property rights cannot eclipse or
impair the inherent background interest in a commons of a
special character on which the plaintiffs' coalitions and the
larger community depend.

Until there is a trial and final decision, an injunction is issued
that prohibits defendant Mython, any of its officers, agents,
and contractors from mining pending completion of a trial.

IT IS SO ORDERED, effective upon entry at the Clerk's Office
and service on the defendant Mython and the attorneys who have
appeared on the record.

From newspaper and e-ticker accounts reported several days later,
Judge Holmes called the direct line of County Sheriff Horace Bentley, rushed down two flights of stairs to the clerk's office, and filed his
dissenting opinion and order one minute before the expiration of the
three-day deadline of the effective date of his earlier order. The clerk
handed Judge Holmes a dozen certified "TRUE COPIES" to deliver
to defendant Mython's head honchos, the supervisors at the dunes,
and Mython's lawyers and lawyers for the coalitions, Solon Creek,
and the other interested parties. In a matter of minutes, Sheriff Bentley pulled up, lights flashing at the judge's private entrance in the rear
of the courthouse.

Judge Holmes stepped outside, still in his judicial robe, squint-
ing at the black, gold-decaled, muscular SUV as the passenger door
swung open and Bentley yelled at him to jump aboard.

The sheriff and his half-robed sidekick, Judge Odie Holmes, the
glare of the mid-morning sun behind them, brighter perhaps because

of the angle of light in Judge Holmes's spirit, sped toward the coast and Voyager Dune. The sheriff's dashboard clock read 10:17 when the roaring squad car, lights flashing and siren screaming, turned and headed north on the county road to the Voyager Dune.

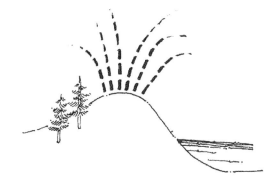

THE FATE OF VOYAGER DUNE

... they saw something
come out of the top of
the dune.

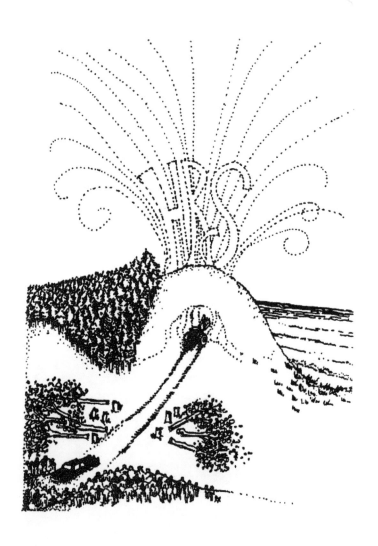

On the morning of the third day after the trial, exactly two weeks from the day of the official announcement of the start of the mining activity, a rumbling could be heard in the distance. It invaded the quiet air and insulted the morning light flooding the treetops at the edge of the field behind the sleepy dune village encampment. Pinkerton guards rubbed their eyes and marched, coffee in hand, to the entrance, badges glinting in the sun. Dune village tents rustled like leaves in a draft of wind as stupefied campers crawled out of their sleeping bags and wiggled into their tapered jeans. The rumbling pressed closer, echoed in the valley where the road disappeared into the hills to the south.

The ground vibrated as a half dozen brightly painted yellow dozers and earth movers the size of four-story buildings rounded the nearest curve, led by a line of Pinkerton cars, yellow lights flashing, and followed by a black stretch limo. The first Pinkerton car pulled up and parked on the shoulder near the entrance. The rest of the convoy of cars and machines turned into the entrance to the dune. The black stretch limo kept going, disappeared down the road to the north, and whipped up a tail of dust as it turned onto a two-track. Engines growled and roared and the dozers, six abreast, lowered their huge blades to the damp earth and peeled the skin of grass from the ground. Shrubs, poplar, and scattered saplings of maple and beech dropped like tackling dummies as the dozers plowed toward the base of the dune. Within fifteen minutes the dozers had cleared a swath to the dune the width of two football fields. Soon after, a twenty-foot-high platform shook as the sand conveyor belt started up and ran from the base of the dune back to the transfer station.

The face of the Voyager Dune resembled a white-tailed deer in the sight of an elephant gun. Tired, bloodshot eyes, thousands of eyes of the campers gazed at the bared flesh of the dune. Men in official garb drove posts into the ground and connected them with yellow ribbon along the front of the dune as if it was a crime scene. The treads of the monster shovel rolled and stopped at the yellow ribbon.

The black stretch limo sped across a field and pulled up behind the giant shovel. Five men and a woman jumped out. The woman positioned the men about the yellow ribbon, stepped back and picked up a camera. The taller, thin man pulled out some gold-plated scissors and with a tightly held smile snapped the ribbon, ends swirling off in the dust-filled breeze.

"Wow, that's a sandbox," the thin man chuckled.

"Amen," said the chubby fellow, spitting out the stub of a cigar as he bowed to the dune in mock prayer.

The ground shook as the thick treads spewed clods of dirt and pounded closer toward the sun-glazed flesh of the dune. The guards, spectators, and campers closed in on the machine. The shovel's massive arm jerked and rose into the air as if executing a deadly salute. The crowd blinked. The machine's arm with the shovel lurched. The elbow opened and the wrist of the steel arm punched outward. The blade of the shovel struck the belly of Voyager Dune with the force of a prize fighter's fist to the gut.

In the distance, the sound of car engines roared, pistons slamming, tires whining and growling like a straight-line windstorm. Thirty fat crows perched on the cap-line of a peak-roofed block-long pole barn near the entrance from the county road. Sirens screamed. A TV helicopter hovered overhead. The crows flapped and flailed. The ground shuddered when the shovel ripped upward, lifting and spilling cascades of sand.

Out of nowhere, a siren-screaming, lights-flashing, black SUV bounded across the field toward the base of the dune. It spun to a halt, spitting a rooster-tail of grass and sand. Out leaped the tall, heavy-set Sheriff Bentley, followed by Judge Odie Holmes, still wearing his robe, flung open and flying in the wind. The two men ran through the crowd toward the black stretch limo and cadre of news reporters.

The men and woman dignitaries behind the machine shook hands. Pinkerton guards puffed out their chests. The crowd gasped. Heads snapped upwards toward the top of the dune. The dune started shaking, something happening at the top of the dune. Sand spun, spit, and churned, a spiraling sun devil. A volcano of sand shot up and outward. A burst of wind spun the dune into a desert sandstorm. Suddenly, the whole front edge of the dune rose and rolled forward like a tidal wave, crashing and burying the machine to the elbow of the arm of the shovel that jerked like the hand of a drowning victim. The two operators leaped from the cab to escape the entombment in the towering shovel; the dignitaries behind the shovel ran in terror as the sand wave closed around them. The crowd stared; eyes didn't blink.

A chorus of oohs and aahs from the crowd sounded like they were watching fireworks on the Fourth of July. Then the chorus fell into what sounded like a meditative *om*. The crowd kept looking up, fell to their knees. A flash of light rocketed upward from the dune. Then something exploded high in the air, spun, and spread across the horizon into a massive cloud, and a soft, translucent yellow dust fell gently on the surrounding countryside. The ball of sun burned pale orange through the haze. All lay silent.

No one knew how long the silence lasted. As suddenly as it had all happened, the Voyager Dune quieted down and dozed placidly in the heat of the late morning sun. The crowd disbanded, walking and holding hands in small groups to their Mound City. Some left filing onto the state highway in their cars, others packed tents and gear into pickups and vans.

Two Mython dignitaries crawled into the back seat of the black stretch limo before it slowly merged with the line of cars as they turned onto the county road that wound through the wooded foothills to the south. The helicopter disappeared over the horizon to the east. Within an hour, only a few tents, smoldering campfires, police cars, and two EMT ambulances remained. A solitary scraggly-haired man crawled toward the roof of a shack half-covered by sand. He crawled past the shack to the crest of the disturbed dune. When he reached the crest, he dug his hands into a strand of coarse dark loamy soil.

Circulation of the newspapers, emails, Facebook and Instagram posts quintupled in the hot August days that followed. Videos showed the cloud of soft golden dust. Headlines read: "Sand Dune Explodes," "Sacred Mound Showers Golden Light," and "Sand Dune Buries Mining Efforts." Another read, "Mysterious Mound Awakens."

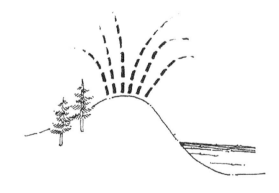

EPILOGUE

The wrinkles have
realigned around their
twinkling eyes …

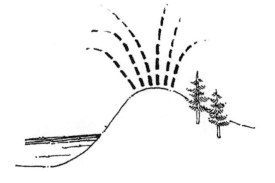

In the years that followed, the Voyager Dune, "Dune," was to locals as if they were talking about a friend, was declared sacred by the state legislature, and designated as a natural and cultural heritage site for the benefit of the tribes and citizens in the area of the country's inland seas. Newspaper reports began to fade, then television news, although drone shots of the mysterious golden haze would pop up occasionally on social media. Mostly, no one wanted to talk about it. It was as if the incident had been buried with the giant shovel. Mython World Mining Corporation abandoned the dune, never to return. Last reports stated that the company gave the Dune to the state for the newly designated sacred and heritage site.

The chairperson of the board of the corporation resigned and moved into a house on the inland sea not far from the Dune.

Solon Creek returned to his shack, cleared the sand that had covered it to the eaves, and resumed his life at the foot of the Dune. Over time he, local tribes, and villagers helped the archeologists dig and mark tools of copper, bones, ornaments of mica, chert, obsidian, and broken pottery with designs. The archeologists confirmed the dark, ocher soil had been placed there by human hands over one thousand years ago.

About seven hundred men, women, and children now live in a village of tiny houses known as Dune Village. The extent and shape of the mound remains a mystery, though those who remember the day the Dune buried the giant shovel have little doubt that it is a spirit mound. The field where the encampment once existed is teeming with a variety of fruits and vegetables, a communal garden, and newly planted pines and hardwoods. In a nearby town, neighborhoods ripped up alleys and tore down garages, replacing them with a row of gardens with wells, parking, and dark red barns for their implements at either end. Signs in white letters on the side of dark red barns read, "Cars into Plowshares."

Judge Odie really did retire from the bench at the end of his term. He and his wife, Harriet, put up a sculpture on the front porch of their home in the City-on-the-Bay, a bronze-colored Lady Justice—no blindfold, scales with a heart, and an olive leaf in place of a sword. As for The Dissenting Opinion of Judge Holmes, thanks to a nomination by a writer and fishing friend, the State Historical Society bestowed the State History Milestone Award on him for calling attention to history and the notion of jurisprudence that encouraged the dedication of the Voyager Dune and its sacred mound. "I accept this award for Solon Creek," he said. It is said that law students, academics, and sometimes wandering poets ask to visit the dune or see the original decision stashed away in the state's archives.

Most of the thousands who lived in the City-on-the-Bay suppressed what happened at the Voyager Dune. It turned into a fuzzy hallucination. "Maybe it was a UFO or something," some people began to say. Others said it was just a dream.

Just a dream? If something is forgotten, treated as if it didn't really happen, is it "just a dream?"

If things are forgotten, erased from memory, are they still part of reality?

In the case of Dune and the golden dust that covered the countryside from what some claimed was the covered sacred mound, what happened that day when the gargantuan shovel pierced the Dune? Perhaps no one will really ever know.

In the shade of warm evenings, Odie Holmes often parks his car, carries a wooden campstool, and sits down next to Solon Creek at his cabin in the ravine at the base of the dune. The two of them sit attentively, their weathered Adirondack chairs facing the Dune, without any sound except the breeze or wind and watch and listen to shore birds, hawks, vultures, and eagles. As the light fades to night, they pour a knuckle of locally distilled bourbon into tin cups, and lift their cups to the spirit of Moluv and Voyager Dune.

During these past few years, the people in Dune Village and on nearby farms and homesteads scattered across the hills have begun to meet in small groups, sitting quietly for long periods, staring at the Dune. They climb its steep face of sand and stop to look at the darker soil with strata of reddish sand at the top of the dune and peer into the sunken hole where the dune had exploded. They hold hands and gaze into the distance at the blazing blue waters of the inland sea. Sometimes they just hug or stare into each other's eyes. Sometimes they sing and dance. One thing less visible: the people living near the Voyager Dune have changed; they look different, nearly unnoticeable, but different. The most striking things, though, are their sparkling eyes and happy faces. Life isn't any easier for them, but there is no tightness, less struggle; their step is lighter. The wrinkles of the older people have realigned around twinkling eyes, erasing the struggle and destruction that once dwelled there. The lines on their faces seem to just laugh and dance, seem to be spreading to other people.

Years passed. Decades passed. All the while the rusting elbow and arm of the entombed giant shovel juts out of the slope of the Dune—artifact or being of a culture buried long ago.

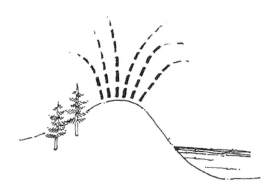

ABOUT PEOPLE OF THE DUNE

The back section of a regional newspaper announces the plans of Mython Corporation, a giant international mining firm, to remove the Voyager Dune, a revered linkage in a rare coastal dune system along the shore of an inland freshwater sea in the middle of North America. Local tribes, residents, conservation organizations, and Solon Creek, a recluse who has lived his entire life in a shack near the foot of the dunes, declare war to save the dune. Solon and the tribes believe there is a sacred mound buried under the shifting sands of the three-hundred-foot-high dune. They tell of ancient Indigenous civilizations who migrated into the area of freshwater seas after the glaciers retreated more than eight thousand years ago. A legend passed down through oral history tells of a civilization around one thousand years ago that built spirit mounds along the shores of these inland seas to restore the vibrant harmonious energy between their people, earth, and the sky. The residents and conservationists believe the Voyager Dune is so rare, unique, and intertwined with their lives that it must remain undisturbed.

When Mython mobilizes its massive mining operation to remove the dune and build a large residential community, resort, and harbor in its place, people from everywhere pitch tents at the base of the dune to block the mining. Soon the few tents grow into a village encampment of thousands. Mython files a lawsuit to remove trespassers and encampment. The tribes form the Mound People Coalition and residents, state, and national organizations form People of the Dune. The two coalitions file a lawsuit to stop Mython's mining and development. The trial ends up in the courtroom of middle-aged, local circuit judge Odom "Odie" Holmes, who, despite his personal predilections, holds a high respect for the principles of the law.

The external forces of the parties' claims collide in a battle between the expectations of private property and the special value of the dune to the tribes and citizens. After his decision that follows the law, he allows the removal of the dune to begin in three days, he is shaken to the core. The night before the mining is slated to start, he experiences a haunting visitation. He drives to the courthouse and climbs the private stairway to his chambers. He must struggle with a decision he is compelled to make: not only must he revisit the fate of the Voyager Dune, but he must face the fate of people and the earth itself.

ACKNOWLEDGMENTS

Appreciation abounds: Thank you to Michael Delp, Stephanie Mills, Dave Dempsey, and Grant Parsons, for reading and comments that enriched the final manuscript; Heather Shaw, for artistic and creative guidance and design, and for everyone at Mission Point Press for their professional support. I'm grateful to Elaine Kozar and the late Sherry Petersen whose original layout and illustrations for *The Mound People* find new life in this new work. And thanks to Tajín Robles for the new illustrations that bring us closer to the beating heart of Lady Justice. A special thank you to my wife, Judy Bosma, who not only smoothed the rough edges of the final manuscript but endured yet another of my sudden compulsions. My continuing gratitude for Hallie (Olson) Wastell—you're with us forever—and Jessica (Olson) Perez, Kathryn (Olson) Bourdon, and Jim Olson Jr. for their help with Water Visions and what inspires us—the common good.

ENDNOTE

Several thousand years ago, ancient peoples built tens of thousands of mounds in and along the valleys of the Upper Mississippi River, Ohio River basins, and the Great Lakes region of North America. As many as fifteen thousand of these mounds have been flattened by the jaws of a new nation's "manifest destiny," a destiny that masticated a continent and its tribal civilizations who had forged over the millennia a view of earth, sky, and spirit as a harmonious relationship without any notion of the meaning of the words, "resource," "property," or "cost-benefit." Perhaps, these mound builders and Indigenous people and the natural world left a pathway of being for all of us that has been there from the beginning, long before the European monarchs "discovered" North America as if it had been divinely ordained.

We owe much to the archaeologists and anthropologists who have spent lifetimes digging and reading the braille from the remnants and marks of the soft-footed civilizations of these ancient people.

We also owe much to those who have spent their careers and personal lives dedicated to the understanding and protection of our dynamic, often fragile coastlines on the oceans and inland seas. Their work has laid the scientific, geological, physical, and ecological basis from their aeolian formation to their stabilization and dynamic changes. These dunes are vulnerable. Slight changes in climate through water levels, precipitation, winds, sediments, and human activities can cause rapid devastating damage or destruction. With the ever-intensifying effects of climate change, seas, lakes, rivers, creeks, shorelines, cliffs and coastal dunes, wetlands and floodplains suffer dramatic changes and damage.

We are indebted to those who for whatever reason gravitated toward or became interested in the protection, preservation, and conservation of what has become, since Earth Day 1970, and to the many resolute academics, scientists, policy wonks, and those environmental lawyers who put their sense of love of nature, a drive for challenges and answers, or the good of others or the environment and life above other demands. There really are no shortcuts.

And we are indebted to the undaunted line of explorers, mystics, saints, monks, religious and political leaders, and the poets, philosophers, writers, artists, scientists, and activists who have risked their lives in search of songs and wisdom that give us clues to the vast diversity of our world's ontology or beingness. They have pointed us toward an understanding—one that has been with us since the ancient people and civilizations—that we need not be the victims of a worldview that things and people are objects, as Judge Odom "Odie" Holmes wrote in his dissenting opinion—a pith-ball experiment gone out of control.

While I have taken the liberty to name some characters in this book after people for whom I have great respect for their dedication and courage to protect earth and others, this book is a work of fiction and the appearance of their names bears no resemblance to them in their real life.

Finally, the following list is, hopefully, representative of the research and reading that may have influenced the story, particularly the dune, the sand mound, dune mining, and the Bench Opinion and the Dissenting Opinion of Judge Odom Holmes.

ABOUT THE AUTHOR

Jim Olson is a lawyer and writer who lives in the Great Lakes region of North America. For five decades, Jim has represented citizens and communities in the courts, and authored articles, papers, and blogs on law and the environment, water, and natural resources. He is a recipient of the Michigan State Bar's Champion of Justice Award and was named Lawyer of the Year by *Michigan Lawyer's Weekly*. In 2010, he founded For Love of Water, a nonprofit law and policy center, to protect the public commons in water, lands, and community. He is a recipient of a Michigan Council of Arts award for writing, and is the author of *Environmental Law, A Citizens Guide* (Neahtawanta Press, 1981), *The Mound People* (Neahtawanta Press, 1984), and a children's book. His filmography includes "FLOW: For Love of Water" (2008), "Blue Gold" (2008), and "Troubled Water" (2019).

BIBLIOGRAPHY & SOURCES

BOOKS

Teresa of Avila, "Interior Castle," *Collected Works,* Washington Institute of Carmelite Studies, 1976.

Maude Barlow, *Blue Covenant, The Global Water Crisis and the Coming Battle for the Right to Water,* New Press, 2008.

Maude Barlow, *Blue Future, Protecting Water for People and the Planet Forever,* Anansi, 2013.

Gregory Bateson, *Mind and Nature: A Necessary Unity,* E. P. Dutton, 1979.

Thomas Berry, *The Dream of the Earth,* Sierra Club Books, 1989.

Wendell Berry, *Another Turn of the Crank,* Counterpoint, 2011.

Michael Blumm and Mary Christina Wood, *The Public Trust Doctrine in Environmental and Natural Resources Law,* Carolina Academic Press, 2013.

Robert Birmingham and Leslie Eisenberg, *Indian Mounds of Wisconsin,* University of Wisconsin Press, 2000.

David Bollier and Silke Helfrich, Editors, *The Wealth of the Commons: A World Beyond Market & State,* Levellers Press, 2012.

Jean Pierre de Caussade, *A Treatise on Prayer from the Heart,* Institute of Jesuit Sources, 1998.

Jean Pierre de Caussade (Kitty Muggeridge, Translator), *The Sacrament of the Present Moment,* Harper Collins, 1981.

Herman Daly, *Steady-State Economics,* Island Press, 1991.

Richard Epstein, *Principles for a Free Society: Reconciling Individual Liberty With the Common Good,* Basic Books, 2002.

Richard Erdoes and Alfonso Ortiz, Editors, *American Indian Myths and Legends,* Pantheon, 1985.

Pope Francis, *Encyclical on Climate Change and Inequality: On Care for our Common Home,* Melville House, 2015, pp. 58–59, 96–97.

Viktor Frankl, *Man's Search for Meaning,* Beacon Press, 1992.

Jim Harrison, "Water," *Saving Daylight,* Copper Canyon Press, 2007.

Ernestine Hill, *Water into Gold,* Angus & Robertson Publishers, 1958.

Oliver Wendell Holmes, *The Common Law,* Little, Brown and Company, 1923.

Robinson Jeffers, "De Rerum Virtute," *Hungerfield and Other Poems,* Random House, 1954.

Robin Wall Kimmerer, *Braiding Sweetgrass,* Milkweed, 2013.

W. Vernon Kinietz, *The Indians of the Western Great Lakes, 1615–1760,* Ann Arbor Paperbacks, Second Printing, 1972.

Naomi Klein, *This Changes Everything: Capitalism vs. The Climate,* Simon and Schuster, 2014.

Aldo Leopold, *A Sand County Almanac and Sketches Here and There,* Oxford University Press, 1949.

John Locke, *Second Treatise on Civil Government,* 1689.

George Perkins Marsh, *Man and Nature,* The Perfect Library, 2015.

Andrew McLaughlin, *A Constitutional History of the United States,* Appleton-Century-Crofts, 1936.

Czeslaw Milosz, "Diary of a Naturalist," *Bells in Winter,* The Ecco Press, 1974.

Czeslaw Milosz, "A Song on the End of the World," *The Collected Poems, 1931–1987,* Harper Collins, 1988.

Mary Oliver, *Evidence: Poems,* Beacon Press, 2010.

Elinor Ostrom, *Governing the Commons,* Cambridge University Press, 2015.

Robert Pirsig, *Lila,* Bantam, 1991.

Robert Pirsig, *Zen and the Art of Motorcycle Maintenance,* Bantam, 1981.

Hanna Plyväinen, *The End of Drum-Time,* Henry Holt and Co., 2023.

Daniel Quinn, *Ishmael,* Bantam/Turner, 1992.

Joseph L. Sax, *Playing Darts with a Rembrandt: Public and Private Rights in Cultural Treasures,* University of Michigan Press, 1999.

E.F. Schumacher, *Small Is Beautiful: Economics As If People Mattered, Twenty Years Later,* Harper and Marks, 1999.

J. P. Seaton, Editor and Translator, *Cold Mountain Poems,* Shambhala, 2013.

Charles J. Shields, *And So It Goes: Kurt Vonnegut: A Life,* St. Martin, 2012.

Theresa Smith, *The Island of the Anishnaabeg: Thunderers and Water Monsters in the Traditional Ojibwe Life-World,* University of Nebraska Press, 1995.

Christopher Stone, *Should Trees Have Standing? Law, Morality, and the Environment,* Oxford University Press, 3rd Edition, 2010.

David Wallace-Wells, *The Uninhabitable Earth: Life after Warming,* Tim Duggan Books, 2019.

Mary Christina Wood, *Nature's Trust,* Cambridge University Press, 2013.

Dean Wooldridge, *The Machinery of Life,* McGraw Hill, 1966.

Andrea Wulf, *The Invention of Nature, Alexander von Humboldt's New World,* Alfred A. Knopf, 2015.

Andrea Wulf, *Magnificent Rebels,* Alfred A. Knopf, 2023.

W. B. Yeats (Richard Finneran, Editor) *The Collected Poems of W.B. Yeats,* Scribner, 1996.

ARTICLES, ESSAYS, AND PAPERS

Margaret Atwood, "How Did Christianity Come Unglued from Nature?" *Broadview,* January 1, 2012.

Bernard Bell, Land, 'Sacred Spaces,' and the Free Exercise of Religion: Musings About Apache Stronghold v United States," *Yale Journal on Regulation,* July 6, 2022 (See *Apache Stronghold v United States,* 38 F. 4th 742 [9th Circ., June 24, 2022]; rehearing granted, vacated, 56 F. 4th 636, Nov. 17, 2022).

Shannon Biggs and Dennie Opal Plant, "Rivers, Rights and Revolution: Learning from the Maori," Blog, Movement Rights, February 13, 2017. https://www.movementrights. org/rivers-rights-and-revolution-learning-from-the-maori/.

Michael Blumm, "Internationalizing the Public Trust Doctrine: Natural Law and Constitutional and Statutory Approaches to Fulfilling the Saxion Vision," *University of California Davis,* Vol. 45, February 2012.

Michael Blumm, "The Public Trust Doctrine Fifty Years after Sax and Some Thoughts on Its Future," 44 *Public Land & Resources Law Review* 1, 2021.

Katharina Bodirsky, "The Commons, Property, and Ownership," *Berghahn Journals,* June 1, 2018; *Stichting FOCAAL and Berghahn Books,* 2018.

Eric Freyfogle, "Private Rights and Collective Governance: A Functional Approach to Natural Resources Law," The Future of Natural Resource Law and Policy Conference, *Getches-Wilkinson Center,* University of Colorado, June 6-8, 2007.

James Olson, "Shifting the Burden of Proof: How the Common Law Can Safeguard Nature and Promote An Earth Ethic," 20 *Environmental Law* 891, 1990.

Carol Rose, "The Comedy of the Commons: Custom, Commerce, and Inherently Public Property," 53 *University of Chicago Law Review* 711, 1986.

Joseph Sax, "The Public Trust Doctrine in Natural Resource Law: Effective Judicial Intervention," 68 *Michigan Law Review* 471, 1970.

Joseph Sax, "What Happens When Trespassing Mink Meet Retreating Geese," *High Country News*, August 14, 1989.

Op Ed, "Climate Disobedience and the New 'Public Trust' Laws of Nature," *Truthout*, May 12, 2016.

UNEP, "Indigenous People and Nature: A Tradition of Conservation," Nature Action, UN Environment Programme, April 26, 2017, unep.org.

Dennis Zotigh, "Native Perspectives on the 40th Anniversary of the American Indian Religious Freedom Act," *Smithsonian Voices, Smithsonian National Museum of the American Indian*, November 30, 2018.

Hartmut Zückert, "The Commons: A Historical Concept of Property Rights," in David Bollier and Silke Helfrich, Editors, *The Wealth of the Commons: A World Beyond Market & State*, Levellers Press, 2012.

Arnold v Mundy, 6 N.J. 1, New Jersey Supreme Court, 1821.

Collins v Gerhardt, 237 Mich 38, Michigan Supreme Court, 1926.

Gunderson v Indiana Department of Natural Resources, 90 N.E. 3d. 1171, Indiana Supreme Court, 2018.

Hudson County Water Co. v McCarter, 209 U.S. 49, United States Supreme Court, 1908.

Illinois Central Railroad v Illinois, 146 U.S. 387, United States Supreme Court, 1982.

In re Water Use Permit Applications, 94 Haw. 97, Supreme Court of Hawaii, 2000.

Lucas v South Carolina Coastal Council, 505 U.S. 1003 (1002).

Montana PPL v Montana, 565 U.S. 576, United States Supreme Court, 2012.

National Audubon Society v Department of Water and Power, City of Los Angeles, 33 Cal. 3d 419, California Supreme Court, 1983.

Obrecht v National Gypsum Company, 361 Mich 399, Michigan Supreme Court, 1960.

Pennsylvania Coal Company v Mahon, 260 U.S. 393 (1922).

Printed in the USA
CPSIA information can be obtained
at www.ICGtesting.com
LVHW071634100724
785137LV00016B/33/J